Topics in Operational Research

Since the end of the Second World War, studies in the field of Management Sciences and Operational Research have developed at an extraordinary speed, and have gained in width and depth.

The present series of books on "Topics in Operational Research" contains contributions from authors who have special expertise in this field. There exist, of course, excellent texts on the theoretical background, but this series fulfils a need for detailed descriptions of simple numerical or algebraic techniques, and for reports on practical experience with these techniques, useful to managers and executives in many branches of social, commercial, and industrial activity. Knowledge of such techniques will be spread more widely by the publications of these monographs, and further development stimulated thereby.

The texts are written in such a way that little, if any, advanced knowledge from any branch of science will be required of the reader and no mathematical knowledge beyond A-level G.C.E. or O.N.C.

The various books in the series should thus be of interest not only to management and engineering personnel, but also to teachers in the later forms in schools, and in colleges, as suggestions for possible syllabuses for introductory courses and as sources of interesting problems and examples.

S. VAJDA

Topics in Operational Research

A series of books under the advisory editorship of Professor S. Vajda of the University of Birmingham

Maintenance, Replacement, and Reliability

Maintenance, Replacement, and Reliability

A. K. S. JARDINE
PhD, MSc, CEng, MIMechE, MIProdE

Department of Engineering Production
University of Birmingham

Pitman Publishing

First published 1973

SIR ISAAC PITMAN AND SONS LTD.
Pitman House, Parker Street, Kingsway, London, WC2B 5PB
P.O. Box 46038, Portal Street, Nairobi, Kenya

SIR ISAAC PITMAN (AUST.) PTY. LTD.
Pitman House, 158 Bouverie Street, Carlton, Victoria 3053, Australia

PITMAN PUBLISHING CORPORATION
6 East 43rd Street, New York, N.Y. 10017, U.S.A.

SIR ISAAC PITMAN (CANADA) LTD.
495 Wellington St West, Toronto 135, Canada

THE COPP CLARK PUBLISHING COMPANY
517 Wellington St West, Toronto 135, Canada

ISBN: 0 273 31654 0

Text set in 10/11pt. Monotype Times Roman, printed by letterpress,
and bound in Great Britain at The Pitman Press, Bath
G3(T335/75)

Preface

The purpose of this book is to introduce ways in which the concept of optimization, through the construction and solution of mathematical models, can be brought to bear on the resolution of decision-making problems associated with the maintenance, replacement and reliability of equipment.

The book is self-contained given that the reader has a knowledge of mathematics of about A-level standard. In order not to complicate unnecessarily the mathematics used in the book, and to highlight the principles associated with optimization in decision-making, the various problems posed and analysed have been kept as simple as possible. By doing so, and then making comments when appropriate about limitations of the problem or the model constructed of the problem, it is hoped that the reader will be in a position where he can, with confidence, construct and solve mathematical models of his own particular problems.

Chapter 1 introduces the rationale behind the formulation and solution of mathematical models of problems to improve maintenance decision making.

Chapters 2 and 3 cover the basic concepts which the reader should be familiar with before he proceeds to the main chapters of the book. Readers having a knowledge of probability, statistics and discounting techniques may wish to omit these chapters, or simply have a cursory glance through them. In Chapter 2 aspects of statistics relevant to dealing with the probabilistic problems covered in the book are presented, and some of the more common failure distributions of equipment are identified. The present value concept which is used when evaluating alternative capital replacement decisions and the economic consequences of other long term maintenance decisions is covered in Chapter 3.

Chapters 4 to 9 cover the main decision areas associated with the maintenance, replacement and reliability of equipment. Within each chapter various problems are specified. The statement of the problem is given, a mathematical model is constructed and the conflicting features of the problem are resolved in order to obtain an optimum. Frequent use is made of illustrations to aid the reader's comprehension of the construction of the model. A numerical example is given which illustrates the solution of the model and, when it is thought of possible benefit to the reader to assist his understanding of the solution, a sample calculation is presented. A "further comments" section is given after each numerical example where any limitations of the problem posed and model constructed are given, along with possible extensions which may be necessary to analyse other similar problems. Many points which are important from a practical viewpoint are also included, for example difficulties of data collection and implementation.

The material in the book is an outgrowth of lectures given to students on postgraduate courses of production engineering, operational research, naval architecture, and quality and reliability engineering, and post-experience courses for engineers of various disciplines and others, such as management scientists, interested in maintenance decision making. Selected topics have also been given to undergraduate students of civil, mechanical, production, electrical and electronic engineering. The way in which the book has been written has thus been influenced by remarks or queries made by these students about the contents of an earlier draft of the book.

If the book is used as a teaching text then many of the further comments sections should generate sufficient ideas for the reader to specify problems different from those given in the text so that he can then practise the construction of mathematical models.

AKSJ 1973

Acknowledgements

I am indebted to Steven Vajda of the University of Birmingham for his many helpful comments on the original draft of the book.

To Jim Gordon of Birmingham I offer my thanks for writing the simulation program used in Chapter 7 (Section 7.5). My thanks also go to Ken Richardson of Monash University, Melbourne, for deriving the downtime formula used in Chapter 8 (Section 8.7) and to my colleagues at Strathclyde and Birmingham Universities who commented at the draft stage on various parts of the book.

AKSJ 1973

To KAY

who disbelieves the possible
optimality of breakdown maintenance

Contents

1 General Introduction

1.1 General survey

The purpose of this book is to introduce to those concerned with decision-making in the general area of equipment maintenance some quantitative procedures useful in improving the performance of the maintenance function. The specific problem areas examined cover decisions relating to the maintenance, replacement and reliability of industrial equipment. We shall also consider decisions relating to the facilities required for maintenance, such as manpower requirements and equipment.

Traditionally maintenance engineers in industry are expected to "cope" with maintenance problems without seeking to operate in an optimal manner. For example, many preventive maintenance schemes are put into operation with only a slight, if any, quantitative approach to the scheme. As a consequence, no one is very sure just what is the best frequency of inspection or what should be inspected and, as a result, these schemes are cancelled because it is said "they cost too much." Clearly there is some form of balance required between the frequency of inspection and the returns from it (for example, less breakdowns since minor faults are detected before they result in costly breakdowns). Throughout the book we will examine various maintenance problem areas, noting the conflicts which ought to be considered, and illustrating how they can be resolved in a quantitative manner, in order to achieve optimal or near optimal solutions to the problems. Thus we will be concerned with indicating ways in which the optimization of maintenance decision-making can occur, where optimization may be defined as attempting to resolve the conflicts of a decision situation in such a way that the variables under the control of the decision-maker take their best possible values. As soon as the term "best" is used it is necessary to define what is meant by it and so possible definitions of best in the context of maintenance will be covered in Section 1.2 of this chapter.

Chapters 2 and 3 are included in the book to give a brief introduction to certain basic concepts which must be understood before we can proceed to determine optimal maintenance procedures. Since uncertainty abounds in the area of maintenance (e.g. uncertainty about when equipment will fail), a knowledge of statistics and probability is required. An introduction to relevant statistics is given in Chapter 2. Chapter 3 deals with the present value concept. When dealing with replacement decisions for capital equipment we take account of the fact that the value now of an amount of money to be spent or received later is less than that amount. The present value concept is used to cover this fact.

The main portion of the book is devoted to the building of mathematical models which are appropriate to different problem situations. The purpose of the mathematical models is to enable the consequences of alternative maintenance decisions to be evaluated fairly rapidly in order to determine optimal decisions in relation to an objective. The problem areas covered are as follows.

Replacement. Chapter 4 covers determination of replacement intervals for equipment whose operating costs increases with use; replacement rules when operating two machines in parallel, one of which acts as a standby; replacement intervals for capital equipment; and replacement intervals for equipment subject to failure.

Inspection. Chapter 5 covers determination of inspection frequencies for complex equipment used continuously; inspection intervals for equipment used only in emergency conditions; inspection times for equipment whose condition can only be determined through inspection.

Overhaul and repair. Chapter 6 is concerned with identifying the best overhaul/repair/replace decision to take for equipment subject to breakdown.

Organizational structure. Chapter 7 covers problems associated with determination of the best mix of equipment to have in a maintenance workshop; the best size and composition of a maintenance crew; the use to be taken of subcontracting opportunities.

Reliability. Chapter 8 is concerned with the use of redundancy in equipment design to meet reliability requirements.

Scheduling and sequencing. Chapter 9 gives a brief mention of the use of network techniques to aid project scheduling since such techniques (e.g. PERT, CPM, etc.) tend to be well known and there is abundant literature discussing their use. The chapter concentrates on sequencing decisions and in particular on determination of sequencing rules for routing jobs through machines.

In order not to complicate unnecessarily the mathematics used in development of the models, various assumptions are made which, in practice, may not always be acceptable. The assumptions are clearly stated but it should be remembered that, in practice, it may be necessary to develop more realistic models. As a result of studying the construction of "simple" models it is hoped that the reader will then be able to extend the models to fit his own particular problems.

1.2 The quantitative approach

The primary purpose of the use of any quantitative discipline, such as industrial engineering, operational research and systems analysis, is to assist management in decision-making by using known facts more effectively, by enlarging the proportion of factual knowledge, and by reducing the reliance on subjective judgement.

In the context of maintenance decision-making there is often very little factual knowledge available. Although there may be severe practical difficulties in getting this knowledge, such information is absolutely necessary for the derivation of optimal maintenance procedures. One of the benefits of quantitative studies which have been performed in the maintenance area (see, for example, Jardine [23] for a report of several case studies) is that factual knowledge, such as the form of breakdown distributions of various equipment, is becoming available.

Many procedures are carried out because the maintenance manager "feels in his bones" that they ought to be performed There is little, if any, objective analysis used to determine these procedures It is hoped that this book will go some way towards reducing the proportion of subjective judgement in maintenance decision-making.

As an early example of quantitative decision-making in maintenance, which highlights the important aspect of selection of objectives, we refer to a study done during the Second World War by an operational research group of the Royal Air Force (see Crowther and Whiddington [14]).

The specific problem was that the desired serviceability of Coastal Command aircraft was seventy-five per cent and this was taken as their measure of maintenance performance. Serviceability was the ratio of the number of aircraft on the ground available to fly plus those flying to the total number of aircraft. Although a seventy-five per cent serviceability was felt to be highly desirable Coastal Command were asked to get more flying time from aircraft. The Coastal Command Operational Research Section was called in to examine the problem.

The section examined one cycle of operation of an aircraft and found that the aircraft could be in one of three possible states:

Flying
In Maintenance
Available to Fly

Serviceability, S, which was the criterion of maintenance performance was then:

$$S = \frac{F + A}{F + A + M}$$

where F, A and M are the average times that an aircraft spent in the flying, available to fly, and maintenance states.

Further examination of the problem revealed that for every hour spent flying, two hours were required for maintenance. Using this information it is possible to determine that for a 75% serviceability only 12·5% of an aircraft's time is spent flying with 25% being spent on maintenance, and 62·5% of the time it is in an available state. However, if the serviceability is reduced to $33\frac{1}{3}$%, then $33\frac{1}{3}$% of the aircraft's time is spent flying with $66\frac{2}{3}$% of its time being spent in maintenance and 0% in the available state.

Thus, simply by aiming for a serviceability of $33\frac{1}{3}$% the flying hours could be considerably increased. Clearly in the environment in which the Coastal Command aircraft were operating the accepted objective of maintenance, namely a high serviceability, was wrong. However, for other environments such as that relevant to say aircraft called upon only on emergencies, a high serviceability objective may well be relevant.

As a result of the above analysis, instructions were given that, whenever possible, aircraft should be in the flying state, thus more than doubling the amount of flying which was originally done prior to examination of the appropriate objective of maintenance.

1.2.1. SETTING OBJECTIVES
One of the first steps in the use of quantitative techniques in maintenance is to determine the objective of the study. Once the objective is determined, whether as maximize profit/unit time, minimize downtime/unit time, maximize reliability subject to a budgetary constraint, etc., an evaluative mathematical model can be constructed which enables management to determine the best way to operate the system to achieve the required objective.

In the Planned Flying–Planned Maintenance study referred to above, Coastal Command's maintenance objective originally was to achieve a serviceability of 75% but the study made it clear that this was the wrong objective and what they should have been aiming for was a serviceability of $33\frac{1}{3}$%.

Also, in the Planned Flying–Planned Maintenance study it was mentioned that a high serviceability was perhaps relevant to aircraft called upon only in an emergency. This stresses the point that the objective which a system is operated to achieve may change through changes in circumstances. In the context of maintenance procedures, the way in which equipment is maintained when there are boom conditions may well be different from the way it should be maintained under conditions of an economic slump.

In Chapters 4–9 the models of various maintenance problems are constructed in such a way that the maintenance procedures which are geared to enable "profits to be maximized," "total maintenance cost to be minimized," etc., can be identified. It must be stressed, however, that when determining optimal maintenance procedures care must be taken that the appropriate objective is being used. For example, it will not be satisfactory for the maintenance department to pursue a policy designed to minimize downtime of equipment if the organization requires a policy designed to maximize profit. The two policies may in fact be identical but this is not necessarily so. This point will be demonstrated by an example in Section 5.3.

1.2.2 MODELS
One of the main tools in the scientific approach to management decision-making is that of building an evaluative model, usually mathematical, whereby a variety of alternative decisions can be assessed. Any model is simply a representation of the system under study. In the application of quantitative techniques to management problems the type of model used is frequently a symbolic model where the relationships of the system are represented by symbols and properties of the system are described by mathematical equations.

To illustrate this model building approach we will examine a maintenance stores problem which, although simplified, will illustrate two of the important aspects of the use of models, namely the construction of a model of the problem being studied and its solution.

A stores problem
A stores controller wishes to know how many items to order each time the stock level of an item reaches zero. The system is illustrated on Figure 1.1.

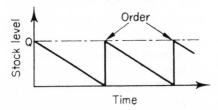

Fig. 1.1

The conflicts in this problem are that the more items he orders at any time means that his ordering costs are going to decrease, since he has to place less orders, but his holding costs will increase. These conflicting features are illustrated on Figure 1.2.

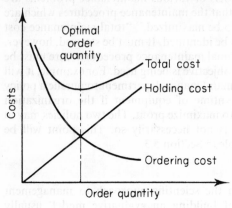

Fig. 1.2

The stores controller wants to determine the order quantity which minimizes the total cost. This total cost can be plotted, as shown on Figure 1.2, and used to solve the problem.

A much more rapid solution to the problem, however, may be obtained by constructing a mathematical model. The following parameters can be defined:

D total annual demand

Q order quantity

C_o ordering cost per order

C_h stockholding cost per item per year

Total cost per year of ordering and holding stock $=$ Ordering cost per year + Stockholding cost per year

Now

Ordering cost/year $=$ Number of orders placed per year
$\times$ Ordering cost per order

$= \dfrac{D}{Q}C_o$

    Stockholding cost/year = Average number of items in stock per year (assuming linear decrease of stock) × Stockholding cost per item

$$= \frac{Q}{2}C_h$$

Therefore, the total cost per year, which is a function of the order quantity, and denoted $C(Q)$, is

$$C(Q) = \frac{D}{Q}C_o + \frac{Q}{2}C_h \tag{1.1}$$

Equation (1.1) is a mathematical model of the problem relating order quantity Q to total cost $C(Q)$.

The stores controller wants the number of items to order to minimize the total cost, i.e. to minimize the right-hand side of equation (1.1). The answer comes by differentiating the equation with respect to Q, the order quantity, and equating the answer to zero as follows:

$$\frac{dC(Q)}{dQ} = -\frac{D}{Q^2}C_o + \frac{C_h}{2} = 0$$

Therefore

$$\frac{D}{Q^2}C_o = \frac{C_h}{2}$$

$$Q = \sqrt{\frac{2DC_o}{C_h}} \tag{1.2}$$

Since the values of D, C_o, and C_h are known, substitution of them into equation (1.2) gives the optimal value of Q. Strictly we should check that the value of Q obtained from equation (1.2) is a minimum and not a maximum. The interested reader can check that this is the case by taking the second derivative of $C(Q)$ and noting that the result is positive. In fact the order quantity is also that at which the holding and ordering costs/year are equal.

Example: Let $D = 1000$ items, $C_o = £5$, $C_h = £0.25$

$$Q = \sqrt{\frac{2 \times 1000 \times 5}{0.25}} = 200 \text{ items}$$

Thus, each time the stock level reaches zero the stores controller should order 200 items to minimize the total cost per year of holding and ordering stock.

Note that various assumptions have been made in the inventory model presented, which in practice may not be realistic. For example, no consideration has been given to the possibility of quantity discounts; the possible lead time between placing an order and its receipt; the fact that demand may not be linear; the fact that demand may not be known with certainty. The purpose of the above model is simply to illustrate the construction and solution of a model for a particular problem. There is abundant literature dealing with problems of stock control where many of these limitations are removed (see for example Hadley and Whitin [19] or Thomas [46]) and the reader interested in stock control aspects of maintenance stores is referred to the standard works.

Along with the problems in stock control suggested above, often decisions must be taken about slow-moving spare parts, where demand occurs infrequently and at irregular intervals. Typically, such spares are expensive to purchase and to hold in stock, and the problem is to decide whether or not to hold a spare at all, but if so, how many. Analysis of such problems is given by Lewis [27] for example.

1.2.3. OBTAINING SOLUTIONS FROM MODELS

In the stores problem of the previous section, two methods for solving a mathematical model were demonstrated, an analytical and a numerical procedure.

The calculus solution was an illustration of an analytical technique where no particular set of values of the control variable (amount of stock to order) were considered but we proceeded straight to the solution given by equation (1.2).

In the numerical procedure, solutions for various values of the control variable(s) were evaluated in order to identify the best result, i.e. it was a trial and error procedure. The graphical solution of Figure 1.2 is equivalent to inserting different values of Q into the model (equation 1.1) and plotting the total cost curve to identify the optimal value of Q.

In general, analytical procedures are preferable to numerical procedures but, because of problem complexity, in many cases they are impossible to use, or impracticable. In the majority of maintenance problems examined in the book, solution of the mathematical model will be obtained by numerical procedures. These will cover primarily graphical procedures, but iterative procedures and simulation will also be used.

Perhaps one of the main advantages of graphical solutions is that they often enable management to see clearly the effect of implementing a maintenance policy which deviates from the optimum identified through solving the model. Also, it may be possible to plot the effect of different maintenance policies together, thus illustrating the relative effects of the policies. To illustrate this point, Chapter 4 includes analysis of two different replacement procedures, namely:

(*a*) replacement of equipment at fixed intervals of time
(*b*) replacement of equipment based on its usage.

Intuitively, one might feel that procedure (*b*) would be preferable since it is based on usage of the equipment (thus preventing almost new equipment being replaced shortly after its installation after a failure, as would happen with procedure (*a*)).

In the case of these different maintenance policies which can be adopted for the same equipment, models can be constructed, as is done in Chapter 4, and for each policy the optimal procedure can be determined. However, by using a graphical solution procedure the maintenance cost of each policy can be plotted as illustrated on Figure 1.3 and the maintenance manager can see exactly the effect of

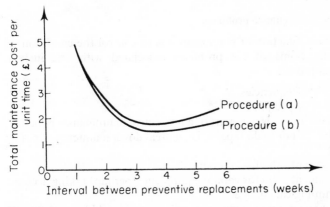

Fig. 1.3

the alternative policies on total cost. It may well be the case that from a data collection point of view one policy involves considerably less work than another, yet they may have almost the same minimum total cost. This is illustrated in Figure 1.3 where the minimum total costs are about the same for procedures (*a*) and (*b*).

Of course, for different costs, breakdown distributions, failure and preventive replacement times, etc., minimum total costs and replacement intervals may differ greatly for different replacement policies. The point is that a graphical illustration of the solutions often assists the manager to determine the policy he wishes to adopt. Also, such a method of presenting a solution is often more acceptable than a statement such as "policy x is the best" which comes after several pages of fearsome-looking mathematics.

Further comments about the benefits of curve plotting are given in Section 4.2.4 of Chapter 4 in relation to the problem of determining the optimal replacement interval for equipment whose operating cost increases with use.

Since trial and error, such as using graphical plots, can be time-consuming we try to get numerical procedures to converge to a solution on successive trials. Such a numerical procedure is termed iterative and all mathematical programming techniques are examples of iterative procedures. One such technique, dynamic programming, will be used to analyse some of the problems of Chapters 4 and 6.

One of the most dramatic developments in numerical procedures, which has been stimulated by computers, is simulation and this will be illustrated in a problem of Chapter 7 relating to the optimal number of machines to have in a workshop.

1.3 Some maintenance problems

The primary function of maintenance is to control the condition of equipment. Some of the problems associated with this include determination of:

Inspection frequencies
Depth of inspection
Overhaul intervals, i.e., part of a preventive maintenance policy
Whether or not to do repairs, i.e. a breakdown maintenance policy or not
Replacement rules for components
Replacement rules for capital equipment—perhaps taking account of technological change
Whether or not an equipment modification should be made
Reliability considerations
Maintenance crew sizes
Composition of machines in a workshop
Spares provisioning rules
Sequence rules for jobs requiring some form of maintenance effort
Scheduling start times for constituent jobs of a maintenance project.

Problems within these areas can be classed as being deterministic or probabilistic. Deterministic ones are those where the consequences of a maintenance action are assumed to be non-random. For example, after an overhaul the future trend in operating cost is known. A probabilistic problem is one where the outcome of the maintenance action is random. For example, after equipment repair, the time to next failure is probabilistic.

To solve any of the above problems there are often a large number of alternative decisions that can be taken. For example, for a component subject to sudden failure we may have to decide whether to replace it while it is in an operating state, or only on its failure; whether to replace similar components in groups when one perhaps has failed, etc. Thus it is seen that the function of the maintenance department is to a large extent concerned with identifying the appropriateness of various decisions to control the condition of equipment to be in line with the objectives of the organization.

1.4 Maintenance control and mathematical models

As indicated above many control actions are open to the maintenance manager. The effect of these actions cannot be looked at solely from their effect on the maintenance department since the consequences of maintenance actions may seriously affect other units of an organization, such as the production unit.

To illustrate the possible interactions of the maintenance function on other departments consider the effect of the decision to perform repairs only, and not do any preventive maintenance, such as overhauls. This decision may well reduce the budget required by the maintenance department but it may also cause considerable production downtime. In order to take account of interactions sophisticated techniques are frequently required and this is where the use of mathematical models can assist the maintenance manager.

Figure 1.4 illustrates the type of approach taken through using a mathematical model to determine the optimal frequency of overhauling a piece of plant by balancing the input (maintenance cost) of the maintenance policy against its output (reduction in downtime).

The above example is very simple and, in practice, there are many factors to be considered in the context of even a single maintenance decision. The above example should, however, suffice to show that the quantitative approach taken in the book is concerned with determining mathematical and statistical relationships between the decisions taken and the consequences which result, in order that the appropriate maintenance decisions may be determined.

The previous comments about the use of models for analysing maintenance problems is very brief, but their use is further outlined later in the book.

Before leaving this section it is perhaps worth noting that the optimal policy indicated in Figure 1.4 does not occur at the cross-over

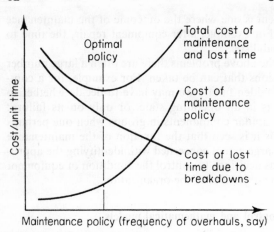

Maintenance policy (frequency of overhauls, say)

Fig. 1.4

point of the two conflicting curves. Very often in the literature when such curves are drawn the minimum is drawn to coincide with the cross-over points. Although this may be the case (as in Figure 1.3) it is by no means always the case and care should be taken when constructing diagrams such as Figures 1.2 and 1.4.

2 Statistical Preliminaries

2.1 Introduction

Decisions relating to a probabilistic problem, such as deciding when to perform preventive maintenance on equipment subject to breakdown, requires information about when the equipment will reach a failed state. The engineer never knows exactly when the transition of the equipment from a "good" to "failed" state will occur but it is usually possible to obtain information about the probability of this transition occurring at any particular time. It is to enable us to deal with such probabilistic problems that a knowledge of statistics is required when optimal maintenance decisions are being determined.

2.2 Relative frequency histogram

If we think of a number of similar production machines subject to breakdown we would not expect each of them to fail after the same number of operating hours. By noting the running time to failure of each machine it is possible to draw a histogram in which the area associated with any time interval shows the relative frequency of breakdown occurring in these intervals. This is illustrated in Figure 2.1.

If we now wish to determine the probability of a failure occurring between times t_x and t_y we simply multiply the ordinate y by the

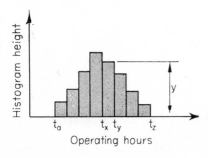

Fig. 2.1

interval $(t_y - t_z)$. Further examination of Figure 2.1 indicates that the probability of a failure occurring between times t_a and t_z, where t_a and t_z are the earliest and latest times at which the equipment has failed, is unity. That is, we assume we are certain of the failure occurring in interval (t_a, t_z) and the area of the histogram equals 1.

2.3 Probability density function

In maintenance studies we tend not to use relative frequency histograms, but rather probability density functions. The reason for this is their easier manageability. Probability density functions are similar to relative frequency histograms except that a continuous curve is used, as illustrated in Figure 2.2. The equation of the curve of the density function is denoted by $f(t)$.

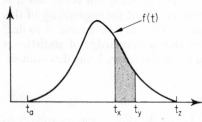

Fig. 2.2

For example, if we have $f(t) = 0.5 \exp [-0.5t]$ we get a curve of the shape of Figure 2.3 and this is termed a negative exponential distribution.

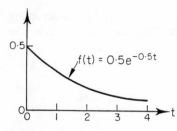

Fig. 2.3

As with the area under a relative frequency histogram, the area under the probability density curve also equals unity.

Referring back to Figure 2.2, the probability of a failure occurring between times t_z and t_y is then the area of the shaded portion of the curve. Resorting to our knowledge of calculus, this area is the integral between t_x and t_y of $f(t)$, namely

$$\int_{t_x}^{t_y} f(t)\, dt$$

The probability of a failure occurring between times t_a and t_z is then

$$\int_{t_a}^{t_z} f(t)\, dt \quad \text{which equals 1}$$

Needless to say, the failure characteristics of different equipment are not the same. Even the failure characteristics of identical equipment may not be the same if they are operating in different environments. There are a number of well known probability density functions which have been found in practice to describe the failure characteristics of equipment and some of them are illustrated in Figure 2.4.

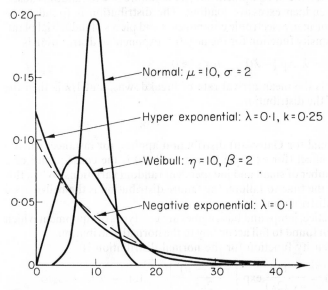

Fig. 2.4

The equations of the four density functions illustrated along with some examples of where these distributions have arisen are as follows.

Hyper exponential
When equipment has failure times which may be very short or very long its failure distribution is frequently represented by the hyper exponential distribution. Some electronic computers have been found to fail according to this distribution. For the hyper exponential distribution the "short" times to failure occur more often than in the negative exponential distribution and similarly the "long" times to failure occur more frequently than in the negative exponential case.

The density function of the hyper exponential distribution is

$$f(t) = 2k^2\lambda \exp\left[-2k\lambda t\right] + 2\lambda(1 - k)^2 \exp\left[-2(1 - k)\lambda t\right]$$

for $t \geqslant 0$ with $0 < k \leqslant 0.5$ and where λ is the mean arrival rate of breakdowns and k is a parameter of the distribution.

Negative exponential
The negative exponential distribution is one which arises in practice where failure of equipment can be caused by failure of any one of a number of components of which the equipment is comprised. Also, it is characteristic of equipment subject to failure due to random causes, such as sudden excessive loading. The distribution is found to be typical for many electronic components and pieces of industrial plant.

The density function for the negative exponential distribution is

$$f(t) = \lambda \exp\left[-\lambda t\right] \qquad \text{for } t \geqslant 0$$

where λ is the mean arrival rate of breakdowns, and $1/\lambda$ is then the mean of the distribution.

Normal
The normal (or Gaussian) distribution applies, for instance, when a random effect (for example, time to failure) is the consequence of a large number of small and independent random variations. When this is so for the time to failure, the failure distribution is the bell-shaped normal distribution.

In practice, lamps and bus engines are two types of equipment which have been found to fail according to the normal distribution.

The density function for the normal distribution is

$$f(t) = \frac{1}{\sigma\sqrt{(2\pi)}} \exp\left[\frac{-(t - \mu)^2}{2\sigma^2}\right] \qquad \text{for } -\infty \leqslant t \leqslant \infty$$

where μ is the mean of the distribution and σ the standard deviation.

Note that for the normal distribution:

$$\int_0^\infty f(t)\,dt \neq 1 \qquad \text{but} \qquad \int_{-\infty}^\infty f(t)\,dt = 1$$

In practice, however, if the mean of the normal distribution, μ, is considerably removed from the origin $t = 0$ and the variance, σ^2, is not too large then it is acceptable to use the normal distribution as an approximation to the real situation. A rough and ready rule would be that the mean μ should be greater than $3 \cdot 5\sigma$ since for this case there would be only about one chance in four thousand of the distribution giving a "negative" failure time.

Weibull

The Weibull distribution is an empirical distribution which appears to fit a large number of failure characteristics of equipment. One of the original papers on the application of the Weibull distribution to equipment failure times related to electron tubes.

The density function of the Weibull distribution is

$$f(t) = \frac{\beta}{\eta} \left(\frac{t}{\eta}\right)^{\beta-1} \exp\left[-\left(\frac{t}{\eta}\right)^{\beta}\right] \quad \text{for } t \geqslant 0$$

where η is a scale parameter (sometimes termed characteristic life), β is a shape parameter, and η and β are positive. When $\beta = 1$ the Weibull is equivalent to the negative exponential; if β takes a value greater than 1 then the Weibull approximates the normal distribution.

Before leaving probability density functions it should be noted that there are other distributions relevant to maintenance studies including, for example, the gamma, Erlang and lognormal. For the density functions of these distributions, and many others, the reader may refer to Hastings and Peacock [21].

2.4 Cumulative distribution function

Frequently in maintenance studies we are interested in the probability of a failure occurring before some specified time, say t. This probability can be obtained from the relevant probability density function as follows:

$$\text{Probability of failure before time } t = \int_{-\infty}^{t} f(t) \, dt$$

The integral $\int_{-\infty}^{t} f(t) \, dt$ is denoted by $F(t)$ and is termed the cumulative distribution function.

As t tends to infinity, $F(t)$ tends to unity.

The form of $F(t)$ for the four density functions described in Section 2.3 is illustrated in Figure 2.5.

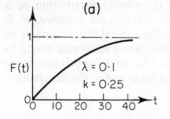
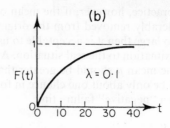

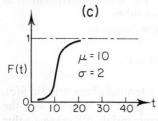
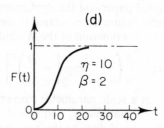

Fig. 2.5 (*a*) Hyper exponential: $F(t) = 1 - k \exp(-2k\lambda t)$
$$- (1 - k) \exp[-2(1 - k)\lambda t]$$

         (*b*) Negative exponential: $F(t) = 1 - \exp(-\lambda t)$

         (*c*) Normal: $F(t) = \dfrac{1}{\sigma\sqrt{(2\pi)}} \displaystyle\int_{-\infty}^{t} \exp\left(\dfrac{-(t - \mu)^2}{2\sigma^2}\right) dt$

         (*d*) Weibull: $F(t) = 1 - \exp\left[-\left(\dfrac{t}{\eta}\right)^{\beta}\right]$

2.5 Reliability function

A function complementary to the cumulative distribution function
is the reliability function, sometimes termed the survival function,
which is determined from the probability that equipment will survive
at least to some specified time, say t. The reliability function is denoted
by $R(t)$ and is defined as

$$R(t) = \int_{t}^{\infty} f(t) \, dt$$

and, of course, $R(t)$ also equals $1 - F(t)$.

As t tends to infinity, $R(t)$ tends to zero.

The form of the reliability function for the four density functions
described in Section 2.3 is illustrated in Figure 2.6.

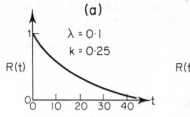

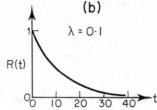

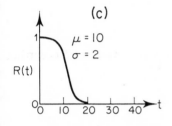

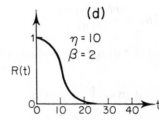

Fig. 2.6 (*a*) Hyper exponential: $R(t) = k \exp(-2k\lambda t)$
$$+ (1 - k) \exp[-2(1 - k)\lambda t]$$

(*b*) Negative exponential: $R(t) = \exp(-\lambda t)$

(*c*) Normal: $R(t) = \dfrac{1}{\sigma\sqrt{(2\pi)}} \displaystyle\int_t^\infty \exp\left(\dfrac{-(t - \mu)^2}{2\sigma^2}\right) dt$

(*d*) Weibull: $R(t) = \exp\left[-\left(\dfrac{t}{\eta}\right)^\beta\right]$

2.6 Failure rate

A statistical characteristic of equipment frequently used in replacement studies is its failure rate.

To introduce the failure rate consider a test where a large number of
identical components are put into operation and the time to failure of
each component is noted. An estimate of the failure rate of a component at any point in time may be thought of as the ratio of a number of
items which fail in an interval of time (say one week) to the number of
the original population which were operational at the start of the
interval. Thus the failure rate of equipment at time t is the probability
that the equipment will fail in the next interval of time given that it is
good at the start of the interval, i.e. it is a conditional probability.

Specifically, letting $r(t)\ \delta t$ be the probability that an item fails during a short interval δt, given that it has survived to time t, then in the usual notation for conditional probability this may be written as

$$P(A|B) = \text{probability of event } A \text{ occurring once it is known}$$
$$\text{that } B \text{ has occurred}$$
$$= r(t)\,\delta t$$

where A is the event "failure occurs in interval δt"
$\quad\quad B$ is the event "no failure has occurred up to time t"

$P(A|B)$ is given by

$$P(A|B) = \frac{P(A \text{ and } B)}{P(B)}$$

where $P(A \text{ and } B)$ is the probability of both events A and B occurring and

$$P(A \text{ and } B) = \int_t^{t+\delta t} f(t)\,dt$$

$P(B)$ is the probability of event B occurring and

$$P(B) = \int_t^{\infty} f(t)\,dt$$

Therefore the failure rate in interval δt is

$$r(t)\,\delta t = \frac{\displaystyle\int_t^{t+\delta t} f(t)\,dt}{\displaystyle\int_t^{\infty} f(t)\,dt} = \frac{F(t+\delta t) - F(t)}{1 - F(t)} \tag{2.1}$$

If equation (2.1) is divided through by δt, and then $\delta t \to 0$ this gives

$$r(t) = \frac{f(t)}{1 - F(t)}$$

where $r(t)$ is termed the instantaneous failure rate (or hazard rate, or force of mortality).

It should be noted that the term failure rate is often used when, strictly, instantaneous failure rate should be used. This, however, should not create any difficulties. Of more importance is the fact that failure rate is sometimes used to describe the steady state rate at which failures occur for a group of similar items where failures are replaced by new items. In this book where failure rate is used we will be referring to instantaneous failure rate.

The form of the failure rate for the distributions discussed in Section 2.3 is illustrated in Figure 2.7.

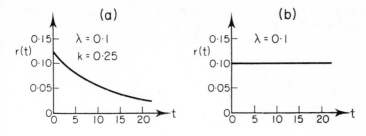

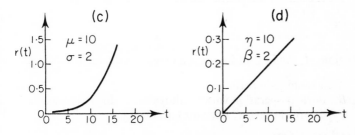

Fig. 2.7 (*a*) Hyper exponential: $r(t) = \dfrac{2\lambda[k^2 + (1-k)^2]\exp[-2\lambda t(1-2k)]}{k + (1-k)\exp[-2\lambda t(1-2k)]}$

(*b*) Negative exponential: $r(t) = \lambda$

(*c*) Normal: $r(t) = \dfrac{\exp[-(t-\mu)^2/2\sigma^2]}{\displaystyle\int_t^\infty \exp[-(t-\mu)^2/2\sigma^2]\,dt}$

(*d*) Weibull: $r(t) = \dfrac{\beta}{\eta}\left(\dfrac{t}{\eta}\right)^{\beta-1}$

An interesting point to note about the hyper exponential distribution is that with an increase in time the failure rate decreases. This may be interpreted as an improvement in the equipment with time and may be the case with equipment which requires small adjustments after an overhaul or replacement to get it completely operational.

When the failure rate increases, such as for the normal distribution, this indicates an ageing or wear-out effect.

With the negative exponential distribution the failure rate is constant. This can be caused by completely random failures and is often the case with complex equipment when failure occurs when any one of a number of independent constituent components fails.

Before leaving this aspect it is interesting to note the form, illustrated in Figure 2.8, which the failure rate sometimes takes with complex equipment. For obvious reasons such a pattern is often referred to as the "Bath-tub Curve".

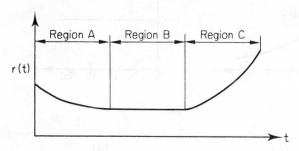

Fig. 2.8

Regions *A*, *B* and *C* of Figure 2.8 may be interpreted as

A   a running-in period
B   normal operation where failures occur due to chance
C   deterioration (i.e. wear out) occurring.

A frequently occurring problem in maintenance is to determine the most appropriate policy to adopt when equipment is in one of regions *A*, *B* or *C*. If the only form of maintenance possible is replacement, either on a preventive basis or on failure, then in regions *A* and *B* no preventive replacements should occur since such replacements will not reduce the probability of equipment failure occurring. If preventive replacements are made in regions *A* or *B* then maintenance effort is being wasted. Unfortunately in practice this is often the case. In region *C* preventive replacement will reduce the probability of equipment failure in the future and just where these preventive replacements should occur will be influenced by the relative costs, etc., of preventive and failure replacements. Such replacement problems will be covered in Chapter 5.

When maintenance policies are more general than only replacement (such as including an overhaul which may not return the equipment to the statistically as good as new condition), then preventive maintenance may be worthwhile in all three regions. Such policies will be covered in Chapters 5 and 6.

2.7 Maintainability

The maintainability of equipment can be defined as the probability that the equipment will be restored to specified conditions within a given period of time T when the maintenance action is performed in accordance with prescribed procedures and resources. Thus, if $f(t)$ is the probability density function of the times required to effect the action (repair, overhaul or replacement), then the maintainability of the equipment is defined as

$$\int_0^T f(t) \, dt$$

Clearly, maintainability is related to the design standard of the equipment.

In practice the log-normal distribution [53] is often a good representation of maintenance action times. However, owing to mathematical difficulties of dealing analytically with the log-normal distribution it is usually approximated to by the negative exponential distribution.

2.8 Further comments

In many practical problems information such as the failure distribution of equipment may not be known. There may however be a set of observations of failure times available from historical records. We might wish to decide which sort of failure distributions to fit to the observations, and what the goodness of the fit is. Thus the failure distribution of the equipment is estimated from a sample of the total information which could conceivably be collected and the goodness of this fit assessed. Discussion of the best methods of identifying probability distributions from a sample is outside the scope of this book. The reader interested in such problems is referred to any of the many statistical textbooks (see [8], [11], [44]), or books on topics such as quality control or reliability engineering (see [38], [40], [41]) which often include chapters dealing with samples, sampling methods, estimation and confidence. Greensted, *et al.* [18] for example, gives numerical procedures for fitting negative exponential, normal and Weibull distributions to sample data. For some probability distributions procedures exist using prepared scaled paper to identify roughly the distribution and estimate its parameters. Such procedures are illustrated by Pieruschka [38] for the negative exponential, normal, Weibull and log normal distributions.

If data in the form of historical records are not available then a specific test or series of tests needs to be made to obtain a set of observations, i.e. sample data. A sample is characterized by its size and by the method by which it is selected. The purpose of obtaining the sample is to enable inferences to be drawn about properties of the population from which it is drawn. For discussion of sample sizes and sampling schemes the reader is again referred to the statistical literature.

The comments above have been made in the context of identifying failure distributions from sample data. Similar points can be made about estimating trend lines, such as the trend in equipment operating costs, from sample data. Again the reader should consult the statistical literature for guidance on identifying trend lines.

3 Present Value

3.1 Introduction

Many maintenance decisions, such as that to replace an expensive piece of plant, involve the investment of large sums of money. The costs and benefits accruing from the investment will continue for a number of years. When the investment of money today influences cash flows in the future and when we are evaluating alternative investment opportunities, account ought to be taken of the fact that the value now of an amount of money depends on when that amount is due, e.g. £1 received in the future is worth less than £1 received now. To enable comparisons of alternative investments to be made we convert the value of monies either spent or received in the future as a result of the investment to its present day value, i.e. we determine the present value (or present worth) of the investment decision. The present value criterion does summarize in one numerical index the value of a stream of cash flows even if we consider an infinite series of cash flows, and so enables alternative investments to be ranked in order of preference; although with some investments decisions the uncertainties of future events are so great that any sophisticated analysis is not worth while.

3.2 Present value formulae

To introduce the present value criterion (or present discounted criterion) consider the following. If a sum of money, say £100, is deposited in a bank where the compound interest rate on such deposits is 10% per annum, payable annually, then after one year there will be £110 in the account. If this £110 is left in the account for a further year there will then be £121 in the account.

In symbol notation we are saying, if £L is invested and the relevant interest rate is i% per annum, payable annually, then after n years the sum S resulting from the initial investment is

$$S = £L \left(1 + \frac{i}{100}\right)^n \tag{3.1}$$

Thus if L = £100, i = 10%, n = 2 years,

$$S = 100(1 + 0·1)^2 = £121$$

The present day value of a sum of money to be spent or received in the future is obtained by doing the reverse calculation to that above. Namely, if £S is to be spent or received n years in the future, and i% is the relevant interest rate, then the present value of £S is

$$PV = £S \left(\frac{1}{1 + \dfrac{i}{100}} \right)^n \tag{3.2}$$

where $\left(\dfrac{1}{1 + \dfrac{i}{100}} \right) = r$ is termed the discount rate.

Thus the present day value of £121 to be received two years from now is

$$PV = 121 \left(\frac{1}{1 + 0·1} \right)^2 = £100$$

i.e., £100 today is "equivalent" to £121 two years from now when i = 10%.

It has been assumed that the interest rate is paid once per year. Interest rates may, in fact, be paid weekly, monthly, quarterly, semi-annually, etc., and when this is the case the formulae 3.1 and 3.2 have to be modified as follows.

If the interest rate is i% per annum, payable m times per year, then in n years the value £S of an initial investment of £L is

$$S = £L \left(1 + \frac{i/100}{m} \right)^{nm} \tag{3.3}$$

Thus the present value of £S to be spent or received n years in the future is

$$PV = £S \left(\frac{1}{1 + \dfrac{i/100}{m}} \right)^{nm} \tag{3.4}$$

It is also possible to assume that the interest rate is paid continuously. This is equivalent to letting m in equation (3.3) tend to infinity. When this is the case:

$$\lim_{m \to \infty} L \left(1 + \frac{i/100}{m} \right)^{nm} = £L \exp \left[\frac{in}{100} \right] \tag{3.5}$$

and the appropriate present value formula is

$$PV = £S \exp\left[-\frac{in}{100}\right] \qquad (3.6)$$

In practice, with replacement problems it is usual to assume that interest rates are payable once per year and so equation (3.2) is used in present value calculations. Continuous discounting is sometimes used for its mathematical convenience, or because it is thought that it reflects cash flows more accurately. If this is the case then equation (3.6) is used.

It is usual to assume that the interest rate i is given as a decimal, and not in percentage terms. Equations (3.2) and (3.6) are then written as

$$PV = £S \left(\frac{1}{1+i}\right)^n \qquad (3.7)$$

$$PV = £S \exp[-in] \qquad (3.8)$$

Both the above formulae will be used in some of the replacement problems of Chapter 4.

An illustration of the sort of problems where the present value criterion is used is the following. If a series of payments $S_0, S_1, S_2 \ldots S_n$, illustrated in Figure 3.1, are to be made annually over a period of n

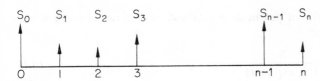

Fig. 3.1

years then the present value of such a series is

$$PV = S_0 + S_1 \left(\frac{1}{1+i}\right)^1 + S_2 \left(\frac{1}{1+i}\right)^2 + \ldots + S_n \left(\frac{1}{1+i}\right)^n \qquad (3.9)$$

If the payments S_j, where $j = 0, 1 \ldots , n$, are equal, then the series of payments is termed an annuity and (3.9) becomes

$$PV = S + S \left(\frac{1}{1+i}\right) + S \left(\frac{1}{1+i}\right)^2 + \ldots + S \left(\frac{1}{1+i}\right)^n \qquad (3.10)$$

which is a geometric progression and the sum of $n + 1$ terms of a geometric progression gives

$$PV = S\left[\frac{1 - \left(\frac{1}{1+i}\right)^{n+1}}{1 - \left(\frac{1}{1+i}\right)}\right] = S\left(\frac{1 - r^{n+1}}{1 - r}\right) \qquad (3.11)$$

If the series of payments of equations (3.10) is assumed to continue over an infinite period of time, i.e. $n \rightarrow \infty$, then from the sum to infinity of a geometric progression we get

$$PV = \frac{S}{1 - r} \qquad (3.12)$$

Using continuous discounting the equivalent expression to equation (3.9) is

$$PV = S_0 + S_1 \exp[-i] + S_2 \exp[-2i] + \ldots$$
$$+ S_n \exp[-ni] \qquad (3.13)$$

Again if the S are equal we have the sum of $n + 1$ terms of a geometric progression which gives

$$PV = S\left(\frac{1 - \exp[-(n+1)i]}{1 - \exp[-i]}\right) \qquad (3.14)$$

If the series of payments is assumed to continue over an infinite period we get

$$PV = \frac{S}{1 - \exp[-i]} \qquad (3.15)$$

In all of the above formulae we have assumed that i remains constant over time. If this is not a reasonable assumption then equations (3.9) and (3.13) need to be modified slightly, for example we may let i take the values $i_1, i_2, \ldots, i_n$ in the different periods.

3.3 Determination of appropriate interest rate

In practice it is necessary to know the appropriate value of interest rate i to use in any present value calculations. Often difficulties are encountered when attempting to specify this value. If money is borrowed to finance the investment then the value of i used in the calculations is the interest rate paid on the borrowed money. If the investment is financed by the internal resources of a company then i

is related to the interest rate obtained from investments within the company. As Wagner [47] says

"The interest rate relevant for a firm's decision-making is an important subject in its own right and is a lively topic of concern among scholars and practitioners of finance."

As far as the present value criterion is concerned we will assume that an appropriate value of i can be specified. Difficulties associated with uncertainty in i can often be reduced by the use of sensitivity analysis and some comments on this are made in Section 4.2.4.

3.4 Example: one-shot decision

To illustrate the application of the present value criterion in order to decide on the best of a set of alternative investment opportunities we will consider the following problem.

A subcontractor obtains a contract to maintain specialized equipment for a period of three years, with no possibility of an extension of this period. To cope with the work the contractor has to purchase a special purpose machine tool. Given the costs and salvage values of the Table for three equally effective machine tools which one should the contractor purchase? We will assume that the appropriate discount rate is 0·9 and that operating costs are paid at the end of the year in which they are incurred.

Machine Tool	Purchase Price (£)	Installation Cost (£)	Operating Cost (£)			Salvage Value
			Year 1	Year 2	Year 3	
A	5000	100	100	100	100	3000
B	3000	100	200	300	400	1500
C	6000	100	50	80	100	3500

For machine tool A
Present value $= 5000 + 100 + 100(0·9)$
$$+ 100(0·9)^2 + 100(0·9)^3 - 3000(0·9)^3$$
$$= £3157$$

For machine tool B
Present value $= 3000 + 100 + 200(0·9)$
$$+ 300(0·9)^2 + 400(0·9)^3 - 1500(0·9)^3$$
$$= £2721$$

For machine tool C
Present value $= 6000 + 100 + 50(0 \cdot 9)$
$$+ 80(0 \cdot 9)^2 + 100(0 \cdot 9)^3 - 3500(0 \cdot 9)^3$$
$$= £3731$$

Thus equipment *B* should be purchased since it gives the minimum present value of the costs.

3.5 Further comments

In the above machine tool purchasing example it will be noticed that the same decision on the tool to purchase would not have been reached if no account had been taken of the time value of money. Note also that many of the figures used in such an analysis will be estimates of future costs or returns. Where there is uncertainty about any such estimates, or where the present value calculation indicates several equally acceptable alternatives (because their present values are more or less the same) then a sensitivity analysis of some of the estimates may provide information to enable an "obvious" decision to be made. If this is not the case then we may impute other factors such as "knowledge of supplier", "spares availability", etc., to assist in coming to a decision. Of course, when estimating future costs and returns, account should be taken of possible increases in materials costs, wages, etc. (i.e. inflationary effects).

When dealing with capital investment decisions a criterion other than present value is sometimes used. For discussion of such criteria, for example, "pay-back period" and "internal rate of return" the reader is referred to the economic literature [16], [30].

4 Replacement Decisions

4.1 Introduction

Replacement problems (and maintenance problems in general) can be classed as either deterministic or probabilistic (stochastic).

Deterministic problems are those in which the timing and the outcome of the replacement action are assumed to be known with certainty. For example, we may have equipment which is not subject to failure but whose operating cost increases with use. To reduce this operating cost a replacement can be performed. After the replacement the trend in operation cost is known. This deterministic trend in costs is illustrated in Figure 4.1.

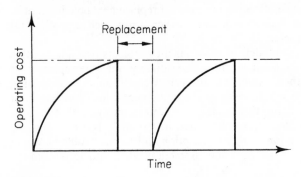

Fig. 4.1

Probabilistic problems are those where the timing and outcome of the replacement action depend on chance. In the simplest situation the equipment may be described as being GOOD or FAILED. The probability law describing changes from GOOD to FAILED may be described by the distribution of time between completion of the replacement action and failure. As described in Chapter 2 (Statistical Preliminaries) the time to failure is a random variable whose distribution may be termed the equipment's failure distribution.

Determination of replacement decisions for probabilistically failing equipment involves a problem of decision-making under one

31

main source of uncertainty, namely: it is impossible to predict with certainty when a failure will occur, or more generally when the transition from one state of the equipment to another will occur. A further source of uncertainty is that it may be impossible to determine the state of equipment, either GOOD, FAILED or somewhere between, unless a definite maintenance action is taken, such as inspection. This aspect of uncertainty, which is probably more relevant to the military field [25] where, for example, the condition of missiles on a site cannot be determined unless an inspection is performed, will be covered in Chapter 5.

In the probabilistic problems of this chapter it will be assumed that there are only two possible conditions of the equipment, GOOD and FAILED, and that the condition is always known. This is not unreasonable since, for example, with continuously operating equipment producing some form of goods we soon know when the equipment reaches the failed state since items may be produced outside specified tolerance limits or the equipment may cease to function.

In determining when to perform a replacement we are interested in the sequence of times at which the replacement actions should take place. Any sequence of times is a replacement policy, but what we are interested in determining are optimal replacement policies, that is, ones which maximize or minimize some criterion, such as profit, total cost, downtime, etc.

In many of the models of replacement problems presented in this chapter it will be assumed, not unreasonably, that the replacement action returns the equipment to the as new condition, thus continuing to provide the same services as the equipment which has just been replaced. By making this assumption we are implying that various costs, failure distributions, etc., used in the analysis are always the same. The exception to this assumption will be the problems where technological improvement of equipment is taken into account in the models.

In cases where we have unlimited lifetime, more or less, and the trends following each replacement action are identical, the interval between the replacements will be constant. This is termed a periodic policy.

Before proceeding with development of replacement models it is important to note that preventive replacement actions, that is, ones taken before equipment reaches a failed state, require two necessary conditions:

(a) The total cost of the replacement must be greater after failure than before (if "cost" is the appropriate criterion—otherwise appropriate criterion, such as downtime, is substituted in place of cost). This may be caused by a greater loss of production since replacement after failure is unplanned or failure of one piece of plant may cause damage to other equipment. For example, replacement of a piston ring in a car engine before failure of the ring may only involve the piston ring charge plus a labour charge, whereas after failure its replacement cost may also include the cost of a cylinder rebore.

(*b*) The failure rate of the equipment must be increasing. To illustrate this point we may have equipment with a constant failure rate. That is, failures occur according to the negative exponential distribution. When this is the case replacement before failure does not affect the probability that the equipment will fail in the next instant, given that it is good now. Consequently, money is being wasted if preventive replacement is applied to equipment which fails according to the negative exponential distribution. Obviously, when equipment fails according to the hyper exponential distribution its failure rate is decreasing and again preventive replacement should not be applied.

It is useful to know that the failure rate of equipment must be increasing before preventive replacement is worth while. Very often when equipment frequently breaks down the immediate reaction of the maintenance engineer is that the level of preventive replacement should be increased. If to start with he determined the failure distributions of the components being replaced he would realize whether or not such preventive replacement was applicable. It may well be that the appropriate procedure is to allow the equipment to break down before performing a replacement and this decision can be made simply by obtaining statistics relevant to the equipment and does not involve construction and solution of a model to analyse the problem.

Note, however, that preventive maintenance of a general nature, which does not return equipment to the as new condition, may be appropriate for equipment subject to a constant failure rate. Determination of the best level of such preventive work will be covered in Chapter 5 in a problem relating to determination of the optimal frequency of inspection and minor maintenance of complex equipment.

Throughout this chapter maintenance actions such as overhaul and repair can be considered to be equivalent to replacement provided it is reasonable to assume that such actions also return equipment to the as new condition. In practice this is often a reasonable assumption and hence the following models can often be used to analyse overhaul/ repair problems. If it is not reasonable to make such an assumption, then the ideas of Chapter 6 (Overhaul and Repair Decisions) may help.

Sections 4.2 to 4.9 cover deterministic problems and stochastic problems are covered in Sections 4.10 to 4.14.

4.2 Optimal replacement times for equipment whose operating cost increases with use: method 1

4.2.1 STATEMENT OF PROBLEM

From time to time, say annually, major surveys are performed on equipment by statutory requirement. Between these surveys the operating cost of the equipment increases due to the deterioration of certain parts of the equipment. Some of these deteriorating parts can be replaced, thus reducing the operating cost of the equipment. The replacements cost money in terms of materials and wages, and a balance is required between the money spent on replacements and savings obtained by reducing the operating cost. Thus we wish to determine an optimal replacement policy which will minimize the sum of operating and replacement costs between the annual surveys.

The conflicts in this problem are illustrated in Figure 4.2.

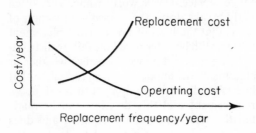

Fig. 4.2

4.2.2 CONSTRUCTION OF MODEL

(1) $c(t)$ is the operating cost per unit time at time t after replacement.

(2) C_r is the cost of a replacement.

(3) The replacement policy is to perform n equally spaced replacements at intervals of t_r between surveys, that is, in interval $(0, T)$ as illustrated in Figure 4.3.

(4) The objective is to determine the optimal interval between replacements to minimize the sum of operating and replacement costs between surveys.

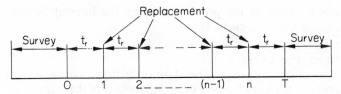

Fig. 4.3

The total cost between surveys will be a function of the interval between replacements, therefore denoting the total cost by $C(t_r)$ we get

$C(t_r)$ = Replacement cost between surveys
$\qquad\quad$ + Operating cost between surveys

Replacement cost between surveys

$\quad$ = Number of replacements between surveys
$\qquad \times$ Cost per replacement
$\quad$ = nC_r

Operating cost between surveys

$\quad$ = Operating cost for each interval between replacements
$\qquad \times$ Number of intervals between surveys

$$= \int_0^{t_r} c(t)\, dt \times (n + 1)$$

Therefore

$$C(t_r) = nC_r + (n + 1) \int_0^{t_r} c(t)\, dt \qquad (4.1)$$

However, n is a function of t_r so, to put n in terms of t_r

$$(n + 1)t_r = T \qquad \text{therefore } n = \frac{T}{t_r} - 1$$

Substituting this into equation (4.1) we get

$$C(t_r) = \frac{TC_r}{t_r} - C_r + \frac{T}{t_r} \int_0^{t_r} c(t)\, dt \qquad (4.2)$$

This is a model of the problem relating the interval between replacements t_r to total cost $C(t_r)$.

4.2.3 NUMERICAL EXAMPLE

(1) Annual surveys are performed on equipment whose operating cost per week after survey or replacement is of the form:

$$c(t) = A - B \exp[-kt]$$

where $A = £100$, $B = £80$, $k = 0.21$. This is illustrated in Figure 4.4a.

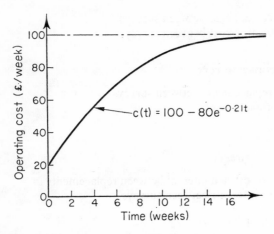

Fig. 4.4(*a*)

[Note: $(A - B)$ may be interpreted as the operating cost per unit time if no deterioration occurs. k is a constant which specifies the shape of the curve.]

(2) C_r, the cost of replacement = £100.
(3) The form of the problem is illustrated in Figure 4.4b.
(4) After substitution of $A - B \exp[-kt]$ for $c(t)$ and integration, the model of the problem (equation 4.2) becomes

$$C(t_r) = \frac{TC_r}{t_r} - C_r + TA + \frac{TB}{t_r k} \exp[-kt_r] - \frac{TB}{t_r k} \qquad (4.3)$$

Since we wish to minimize total cost we differentiate $C(t_r)$ with respect to t_r and equate to zero:

$$\frac{dC(t_r)}{dt_r} = -\frac{TC_r}{t_r^2} + \frac{TB}{t_r k}(-k \exp[-kt_r])$$

$$+ \exp[-kt_r]\left(-\frac{TB}{t_r^2 k}\right) + \left(\frac{TB}{t_r^2 k}\right)$$

Therefore

$$0 = \frac{T}{t_r}\left(-\frac{C_r}{t_r} - B\exp[-kt_r] - \frac{B}{kt_r}\exp[-kt_r] + \frac{B}{kt_r}\right)$$

Since T/t_r is not zero the expression within the brackets must equal zero. This gives

$$\frac{B}{k} - C_r = \left(Bt_r + \frac{B}{k}\right)\exp[-kt_r] \qquad (4.4)$$

Since the values of B, k, and C_r are known the only unknown in equation (4.4) is t_r. The optimal interval between replacements is therefore that value of t_r which makes the left-hand side of (4.4) equal to its right-hand side.

Fig. 4.4(*b*)

Solution of equation (4.4) *and example*

Various numerical methods can be adopted to solve equation (4.4), but the one adopted here is the graphical plot. Using the data of the example the method is:

   (i) Evaluate the left-hand side of (4.4) and mark-off this value on the *y*-axis of Figure 4.5.

  (ii) Evaluate the right-hand side of (4.4) for various values of t_r and plot these values (see Figure 4.5).

 (iii) Draw a horizontal line from the value of the left-hand side until it intersects the curve, then drop a vertical line to the *x*-axis. The point of intersection of the *x*-axis gives the optimal value of t_r as 4·75 weeks.

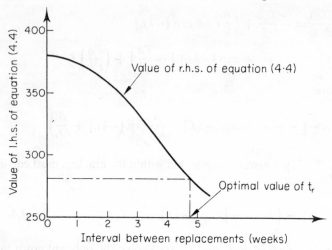

Fig. 4.5

Substitution of $t_r = 4.75$ weeks along with values of A, B, C_r, T and k into the total cost equation (4.3) gives the total cost per year for a policy of replacing every 4·75 weeks as:

$$C(4.75) = \frac{52 \times 100}{4.75} - 100 + 52 \times 100$$

$$+ \frac{52 \times 80}{4.75 \times 0.21} \exp\left[-0.21 \times 4.75\right] - \frac{52 \times 80}{4.75 \times 0.21}$$

$$= £3562$$

Figure 4.6 illustrates the trend of the total cost curve (equation 4.3) for various replacement intervals. The effect on total cost of various replacement policies can be seen very clearly.

4.2.4 FURTHER COMMENTS

A method has now been developed whereby, for particular assumptions, the optimal interval between replacements can be obtained. In practice there may be considerable difficulty in scheduling replacements to occur at their optimal time, or in getting the values of some of the parameters required for the analysis. To further assist the engineer in deciding what his replacement policy should be it is usually useful to plot the total cost curve (see Figure 4.6). The advantage of the curve is that, along with giving the optimal value of t_r, it shows the form of the total cost around the optimum. If the curve is fairly flat around the optimum it is not really very important that the engineer should plan for the replacements to occur exactly at the optimum, thus giving some leeway in scheduling the work. Thus in Figure 4.6 a replacement interval of somewhere between values of t_r equal to 3·5 and 6 weeks does not influence greatly the total cost. Of course, if the total cost curve was not fairly flat around the optimum but rising rapidly on both sides, then the optimal interval should be adhered to if at all possible.

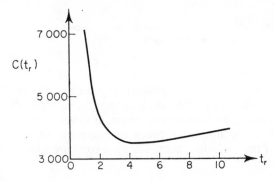

Fig. 4.6

If there is uncertainty about the value of a particular parameter required in the analysis, say we are not sure what the replacement cost is, then evaluation of the total cost curve for various values of the uncertain parameter, and noting the effect of this variation on the optimal solution, often goes a long way towards deciding what policy should be adopted and if the particular parameter is important from a solution viewpoint. For example, varying C_r in equation (4.3) may produce curves similar to Figure 4.7 which demonstrate, in this instance, that although C_r is varied it does not greatly influence the optimal values of t_r. In fact, there is an overlap which indicates a good solution independent of the true value of C_r (provided this value is within the bounds specified by the two curves). If changes in C_r drastically altered the solution from the point of replacement interval and minimal total cost then it would be clear that a careful study would be required to identify the true value of C_r to be used when solving the model. (For example, does C_r include only material and labour costs? Or does it include lost production costs? Or costs associated with having to use less efficient plant, overtime, or use of contractors, etc. to make up losses incurred resulting from the replacement?) Although the decision which can be taken (in this case interval between replacements) essentially may remain constant within the uncertainty region

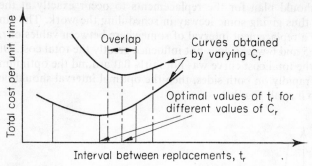

Fig. 4.7

checked by sensitivity, this does not necessarily mean that the true total costs will have, more or less, the same numerical value within the "overlap" region. From a decision-making point, however, this does not matter since it is the interval between replacements which is under the control of the decision-maker. The total costs are a consequence of the decision taken.

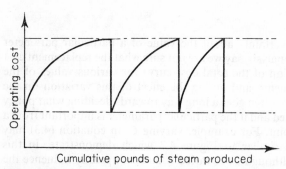

Fig. 4.8

Thus it is seen that a sensitivity check gives guidance on what information is important from a decision making viewpoint and consequently what information should be gathered in a data collection scheme. The statement "garbage in = garbage out" (GIGO), which is frequently made with reference to data requirements of quantitative techniques, is also demonstrated to be not necessarily correct. The validity of GIGO does depend on the sensitivity of the solution to particular garbage. Note, therefore, that GI does not necessarily equal GO and so our information requirements for the use of quantitative techniques may not be as severe as is often claimed.

The replacement problem we have been discussing is similar to a problem associated with boiler plant. Through use, the heat transfer surfaces within the boiler become less efficient and to increase their efficiency they can be cleaned. Cleaning thus increases heat transfer, and less fuel is required to produce a given amount of steam. However, due to deterioration of other parts of the boiler plant the trend in operating cost is not constant after each cleaning operation (equivalent to a replacement) but follows a trend similar to that of Figure 4.8. Thus k in 4.2.3(1) is no longer constant but varies from replacement to replacement. That is, the trend in operating cost after each replacement depends on the amount of steam produced up to the replacement. A detailed study of this problem is given by Davidson [15] who analyses it using a dynamic programming model.

4.3 Optimal replacement times for equipment whose operating cost increases with use: method 2

4.3.1 STATEMENT OF PROBLEM

The problem of this section is identical to that of 4.2 except that the objective is to determine the replacement interval that minimizes total cost per unit time, rather than between the two points $(0, T)$ as in 4.2.

When dealing with optimization problems, in general, we wish to optimize some measure of performance over a long period of time. In many situations this is equivalent to optimizing the measure of performance per unit time, which mathematically is often easier to deal with. We will first construct and solve the model of this problem, which will demonstrate that in this case the two criteria are equivalent.

4.3.2 CONSTRUCTION OF MODEL

(1) The trend in operating cost $c(t)$ and replacement cost C_r are as defined in 4.2.2.

(2) The replacement policy is to perform replacements at intervals of length t_r. The policy is illustrated in Figure 4.9.

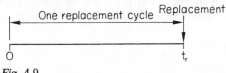

Fig. 4.9

(3) The objective is to determine the optimal interval between replacements to minimize the total cost of operation and replacement per unit time.

The total cost per unit time $C(t_r)$, for replacement at time t_r, is

$$C(t_r) = \frac{\text{Total cost in interval } (0, t_r)}{\text{Length of interval}}$$

Total cost in interval = Cost of operating + Cost of replacement

$$= \int_0^{t_r} c(t) \, dt + C_r$$

$$C(t_r) = \frac{1}{t_r} \left[\int_0^{t_r} c(t) \, dt + C_r \right] \tag{4.5}$$

This is a model of the problem relating replacement interval t_r to total cost per unit time $C(t_r)$.

4.3.3 NUMERICAL EXAMPLE
Using the same data as for the sample of 4.2.3 we get

$$C(t_r) = \frac{1}{t_r} \left[\int_0^{t_r} (100 - 80 \exp\,[-0{\cdot}21t]) \, dt + 100 \right]$$

Evaluation of the above model for different values of t_r gives Table 4.1. This indicates that the optimal value of t_r is five weeks, which is the same as the solution in 4.2.3 if 4·75 is rounded up to the nearest integer. (Remember also that no replacement was made at the end of the last cycle in the problem of 4.2—see also proof of section 4.6.5.)

Table 4.1

t_r	1	2	3	4	5	6	7
$C(t_r)$	127·8	84·7	74·0	70·9	70·5	71·5	72·5

4.3.4 FURTHER COMMENTS
In construction of the models of this and the previous section the time required to effect a replacement has not been included. This replacement time can be catered for without difficulty (see Figure 4.10

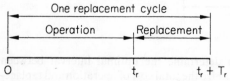

Fig. 4.10

and equation (4.6) which is the appropriate model). In practice it is often not unreasonable to neglect the replacement time provided it is small when compared to the interval between the replacements.

$$C(t_r) = \frac{\int_0^{t_r} c(t)\, dt + C_r}{t_r + T_r} \tag{4.6}$$

4.4 Optimal replacement policy for equipment whose operating cost increases with use: finite time horizon

4.4.1 STATEMENT OF PROBLEM
In the examples of sections 4.2 and 4.3 it was assumed that equipment would be used over a long period of time. The problem of this section is similar to the previous ones, namely if operating costs are increasing then the operating costs can be reduced by replacement. The assumption is not made, however, that the equipment will be used for a long time period but only that it will be used over a fixed future period of time. This is the sort of situation that might occur if a machine is producing goods according to a production plan and we wish to determine the best operating/replacement policy over the period which the machine is to be used.

The specific objective is to determine an optimal replacement policy (i.e. sequence of decisions) which tells us, when equipment reaches a particular age, whether or not it should be replaced or continue to be operated to minimize the total cost of operation and replacement over a fixed future period of time.

4.4.2 CONSTRUCTION OF MODEL

(1) I is the age of the equipment since it was last replaced and with n periods of time to go until the end of the production plan.
(2) $c(a)$ is the cost of operating equipment for one period of time when the equipment is of age a since last replaced at the start of the operating period.
(3) J is the age of the equipment since last replaced with $(n-1)$ periods of time to go to the end of the production plan.
(4) C_r is the cost of replacement.
(5) $C(I, J)$ is the total cost of starting with equipment of age I at the start of a period and having equipment of age J at the end of the period.
(6) The objective is to perform replacements in such a way that the total cost of operating and replacing the equipment, $C_n(I)$, over

next *n* periods of time is minimized when equipment is of age *I* at the start.

When $C_n(I)$ takes its minimum value, this smallest cost is defined as $f_n(I)$.

The sort of policy that will result from the analysis is illustrated in Figure 4.11 where, with ten weeks to go, the equipment is of age three weeks since last replaced. This may be interpreted as follows.

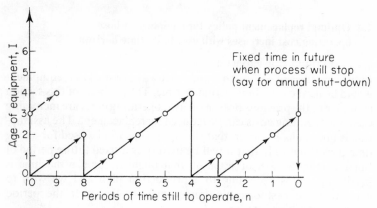

Fig. 4.11

With ten weeks to go there are two decisions possible: CONTINUE OPERATING or REPLACE. If the decisions taken is to CONTINUE then the equipment will be of age 4 when a decision can next be taken and this "move" is illustrated by the dotted line in Figure 4.11. The cost of the decision to continue is the cost of operating equipment for one period when equipment is of age 3 at the start of the period and this can be illustrated as in Figure 4.12.

```
I = 3                         J = 4
|        C(I,J) = C(3,4)        |
|------------------------------>|                 C(3,4) = c(3)
┌──────────────────────────────┐
10                             9
```

Fig. 4.12

If the decision taken is to REPLACE then at the end of the period the equipment will be of age 1. The full-line between period 10 and 9 in Figure 4.11 represents this decision. (Note that it is assumed that the time required to effect the replacement can be ignored. This is not unreasonable since replacement can often take place during a weekend

shut-down rather than during normal operating hours. If this is not
the case the time required to perform replacement can be incorporated
into the model without difficulty—see example in Section 4.5.) The
total cost resulting from the decision to replace is replacement cost
plus the operating cost for one period of equipment which is of age 0,
i.e. new, at the start of the period. This is illustrated in Figure 4.13.

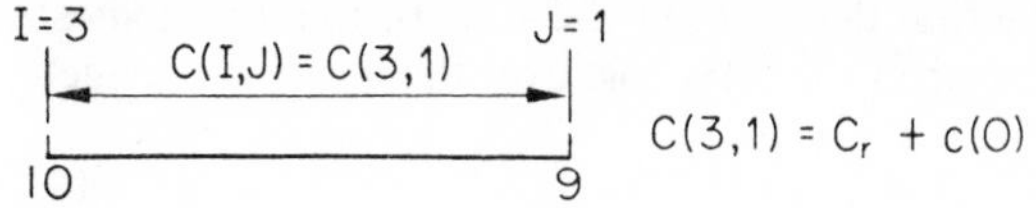

$$I = 3 \qquad\qquad J = 1$$
$$\underset{\rule{0pt}{0pt}\text{IO}}{\vdash}\!\!\!\underset{}{\overset{C(I,J) = C(3,1)}{\rule{3cm}{0pt}}}\!\!\!\underset{\rule{0pt}{0pt}9}{\dashv}$$

$$C(3,1) = C_r + c(0)$$

Fig. 4.13

Thus if equipment is of age 3, with 10 periods to go, and the decision
is taken to replace, then Figure 4.11 illustrates the "path" taken by the
equipment when the replacement policy is to replace the equipment
with ten/eight/four/three weeks to go.

There are, of course, many other replacement policies which could
be adopted and the problem is to identify the best policy.

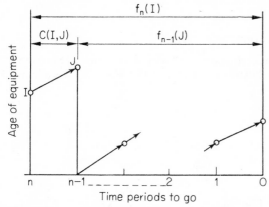

Fig. 4.14

With reference to Figure 4.14 the model used to identify this best
policy is formulated as follows:

$f_n(I) =$ (minimal) Cost resulting from the best decision
    taken at the start of the nth period plus cost of best
    decisions taken over the remaining $(n - 1)$ periods

$C(I, J) =$ Cost resulting from the decision taken at the
    start of the nth period

We then start with a new problem of having equipment of age J at the end of a period and wishing to determine the replacement policy which minimizes the total cost over the remaining $(n-1)$ periods. This minimal cost is $f_{n-1}(J)$.

Thus the total cost over the n periods considered is

$$C(I, J) + f_{n-1}(J)$$

Since we wish to take that decision, at the start of the n periods still remaining, which minimizes the total cost over the n periods, we get

$$f_n(I) = \min_J [C(I, J) + f_{n-1}(J)] \qquad (4.7)$$

with

$$f_0(I) = 0$$

and where J is taken over the possible ages the equipment can have at the end of a period. In this case, $J = I + 1$ or 0. This is a model of the problem relating current age I with n periods to go, to total cost $f_n(I)$.

Equation (4.7) can be solved recursively to identify the best decisions.

4.4.3 NUMERICAL EXAMPLE

(1) The trend in operating costs per period for a machine is given in Table 4.2 and illustrated in Figure 4.15a. Note that it is assumed

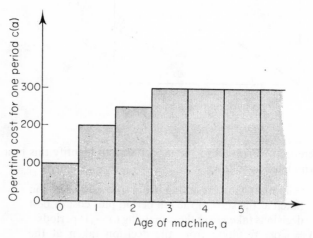

Fig. 4.15(a)

that once the machine is of age 3 the operating cost levels off and remains constant.

Table 4.2

Age of machine since last replaced, a	0	1	2	$\geqslant 3$
Operating cost for one period $c(a)$ (£)	100	200	250	300

(2) The cost of replacement $C_r = £125$.

(3) The total cost matrix for equipment being of age *I* at the start of a period and finishing with age *J* at the end of that period can then be determined as:

I/J	0	1	2	3
0	∞	100	∞	∞
1	∞	225	200	∞
2	∞	225	∞	250
3	∞	225	∞	300

The above cost matrix is obtained as follows.

If equipment is of age 0 at the start of a period we cannot take a decision to go from age 0 to 0 in one period, or from 0 to 2 in one period, or from 0 to 3 in one period.

When it is impossible to go from one age to another in one period then a cost of infinity is inserted in the matrix. As we shall see, this ensures that those impossible decisions do not appear as part of the replacement policy.

If equipment is of age 0 at the start of a period we can take a decision to go from age 0 to 1 in one period. This would occur if the decision CONTINUE OPERATING is taken and the cost is

$$C(0, 1) = c(0) = £100$$

If equipment is of age 1 at the start of a period we cannot go from 1 to 0 in one period, or from 1 to 3.

We can go from 1 to 1 in one period, if the decision REPLACE is taken. The cost of this is

$$C(1, 1) = C_r + c(0) = 125 + 100 = £225$$

We can go from 1 to 2 in one period if the decision CONTINUE is taken. The cost is

$$C(1, 2) = c(1) = £200$$

In a similar way the other elements in the matrix can be obtained.

Note that the matrix needs to be constructed only for values of I and J up to 3 since equipment of age greater than 3 is equivalent, from an operating cost point, to equipment of age 3. This is why it is possible to have a cost for $C(3, 3)$. This really means that the decision is taken to CONTINUE for equipment of age 3 at the start of the period but the operating cost of going from state 3 to 4 is the same as going from state 3 to 3 (see Figure 4.15(a)).

(4) The problem is to determine the replacement policy to be adopted if equipment is new now and there are 4 periods of time to go to complete the production plan.

Equation (4.7) is: $f_n(I) = \displaystyle\min_J [C(I, J) + f_{n-1}(J)]$.

Now, when there is 0 time period to go:

$$f_0(I) = 0 \text{ for all possible values of } I$$

When there is 1 time period to go:

$$f_1(I) = \min_J [C(I, J) + f_0(J)]$$

But $f_0(J) = 0$, therefore

$$f_1(I) = \min_J [C(I, J)]$$

With 1 period to go there are 4 possible values which I can take, i.e. $I = 0, 1, 2$ or 3.

When $I = 0$ (i.e. equipment is new), then

$$f_1(0) = \min_J [C(0, J)]$$

$$= \min \begin{bmatrix} C(0, 0) \\ C(0, 1) \\ C(0, 2) \\ C(0, 3) \end{bmatrix} = \min \begin{bmatrix} \infty \\ 100 \\ \infty \\ \infty \end{bmatrix} \leftarrow \text{i.e. CONTINUE}$$

When $I = 1$ (i.e. equipment is one period old), then

$$f_1(1) = \underset{J}{\min} [C(1, J)]$$

$$= \min \begin{bmatrix} C(1, 0) \\ C(1, 1) \\ C(1, 2) \\ C(1, 3) \end{bmatrix} = \min \begin{bmatrix} \infty \\ 225 \\ 200 \\ \infty \end{bmatrix} \leftarrow \text{i.e. CONTINUE}$$

The situation if $I = 1$, with one period to go, is illustrated in Figure 4.15*b* where it is seen that if the minimum total cost occurs when

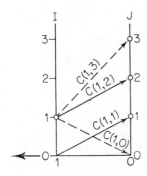

Fig. 4.15(*b*) $C(1, 3) = \infty$ since impossible
$C(1, 2) = c(1) = 200$, i.e. continue
$C(1, 1) = C_r + c(0) = 225$, i.e. replace then operate
$C(1, 0) = \infty$ since impossible

$J = I + 1$ then the best decision is CONTINUE, whereas if the minimum occurs at $J = 1$ then the best decision is REPLACE.

In a similar method to the above it can be identified that
when $I = 2$, then the best value of J is 1, i.e. REPLACE
when $I = 3$, then the best value of J is 1, i.e. REPLACE
The decisions so far identified can be set out as in Table 4.3.
When there are 2 periods to go then equation (4.7) becomes

$$f_2(I) = \underset{J}{\min} [C(I, J) + f_1(J)]$$

Table 4.3

Age of equipment with one period to go, I	0	1	2	3	
Age of equipment at end of period J	1	2	1	1	1 period to go
Action to take at start of period	CONTINUE	CONTINUE	REPLACE	REPLACE	
Minimum total cost $f_1(I)$	100	200	225	225	

When $I = 0$, then

$$f_2(0) = \min \begin{bmatrix} C(0, 0) + f_1(0) \\ C(0, 1) + f_1(1) \\ C(0, 2) + f_1(2) \\ C(0, 3) + f_1(3) \end{bmatrix} = \min \begin{bmatrix} \infty + 100 \\ 100 + 200 \\ \infty + 225 \\ \infty + 225 \end{bmatrix}$$

$$= \min \begin{bmatrix} \infty \\ 300 \\ \infty \\ \infty \end{bmatrix} \leftarrow \text{i.e. CONTINUE}$$

Note $f_1(0), f_1(1), f_1(2), f_1(3)$ are obtained from Table 4.3.

Similarly when $I = 1, 2$, and 3 the best values of J can be calculated to be 1 or 2, 1, and 1. Thus the decisions to be taken when there are 2 periods to go are as in Table 4.4.

When there are 3 periods to go then equation (4.7) becomes

$$f_3(I) = \frac{\min}{J} \left[C(I, J) + f_2(J) \right]$$

Calculation can be performed in the same way as for $f_2(I)$ to give Table 4.5.

Table 4.4

Age of equipment with 2 periods to go, I	0	1	2	3	
Age of equipment at end of period, J	1	1 or 2	1	1	2 periods to go
Action to take at start of period	CONTINUE	REPLACE or CONTINUE	REPLACE	REPLACE	
Minimum total cost $f_2(I)$	300	425	425	425	

Table 4.5

Age of equipment with 3 periods to go, I	0	1	2	3	
Age of equipment at end of period, J	1	2	1	1	3 periods to go
Action to take at start of period	CONTINUE	CONTINUE	REPLACE	REPLACE	
Minimum total cost $f_3(I)$	525	625	650	650	

When there are 4 periods to go then equation (4.7) becomes

$$f_4(I) = \min_J [C(I, J) + f_3(J)]$$

the solution of which gives Table 4.6.

Table 4.6

Age of equipment with 4 periods to go, I	0	1	2	3	
Age of equipment at end of period, J	1	2 or 1	1	1	4 periods to go
Action to take at start of period	CONTINUE	CONTINUE or REPLACE	REPLACE	REPLACE	
Minimum total cost $f_4(I)$	725	850	850	850	

From these four tables it is seen that, starting with new equipment ($I = 0$) with four periods to go, the replacement policy to minimize the total cost of replacement and operation over the four periods is as shown in Table 4.7.

Table 4.7

Periods to go	4	3	2	1
Decision	CONTINUE	CONTINUE	REPLACE	CONTINUE
	(Table 4.6)	(Table 4.5)	(Table 4.4)	(Table 4.3)

The total cost is £725. The policy is illustrated in Figure 4.16.

Construction of Tables 4.3 to 4.6 gives replacement policies for many other situations. For example, if we had equipment of age 1 and

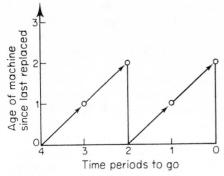

Fig. 4.16

the total production period remaining is 3 periods, then the appropriate policy would be as shown in Table 4.8. The total cost is £625.

Table 4.8

Periods to go	3	2	1
Action	CONTINUE	REPLACE	CONTINUE
	(Table 4.5)	(Table 4.4)	(Table 4.3)

On the other hand, if we start off with equipment which is of age 1, with 4 periods to go, then an appropriate replacement policy is shown in Table 4.9. The total cost is £850.

Table 4.9

Periods to go	4	3	2	1
Action	REPLACE	CONTINUE	REPLACE	CONTINUE
	(Table 4.6)	(Table 4.5)	(Table 4.4)	(Table 4.3)

4.4.4 FURTHER COMMENTS

The previous example assumed that the future operating time of the equipment is known. This may be the case but on the other hand it may not be known. When the time horizon is not known the procedure we have been adopting (known as dynamic programming D.P.) can still be applied by using an estimate of the future operating period to obtain a replacement decision rule. As time goes on, then the calculations can be repeated using any new estimate of the future operating time of the equipment. This approach of updating the time horizon as new information becomes available would not have resulted in any significant reduction in the total operating and replacement cost of the equipment, had the future operating period been known when the calculations were first performed.

The example also assumed that the cost of a replacement remained constant whatever the age of the equipment when replaced. In practice a replacement may be more costly the older equipment becomes since more parts need to be replaced or because there is a decrease in the salvage value of the equipment. This extension can be handled without difficulty using the D.P. approach.

A further assumption in the example was that the time to effect a replacement could be neglected since replacement would take place during a weekend shut-down. When dealing with continuously operating plant this is not a realistic assumption The inclusion in the analysis of replacement time will be demonstrated in the following section (4.5).

When there is only one machine in operation and the time required to make the replacement is to be included, then the cost matrix has to take into account any costs due to the replacement time. Thus if the replacement took one period of time the cost of the decision REPLACE would be the cost of the replacement itself plus perhaps a further cost such as lost production cost, cost of using a subcontractor, cost of using less efficient plant, etc.

In conclusion the following three paragraphs are taken directly from White [48] since they give a very lucid description of the benefits of a D.P. approach to replacement problems in particular and many maintenance problems in general.

"It is perhaps worth emphasizing a conceptual advantage of D.P. . . . It is traditional among some diehards to take the attitude that what matters to some extent when deciding when to replace a piece of equipment is the amount of use we have got out of it so far. They are loth to replace a piece of equipment for the sole reason that 'we have only recently paid £5000 for it and must get some use out of it before we replace'. This point of view is retrospective and conflicts most strikingly with the governing principle of optimality (*the basis of D.P.*) which states that 'it is future performance that matters,' and if, economically speaking, a replacement is justified, since it will minimize the future operating costs, then what we have already paid for it should not matter in the least.

This attitude exists in the context of depreciation policies, which write off the equipment in a more or less arbitrary manner and inject a correspondingly arbitrary value of the equipment to the company at any point in time. Apart from the tax reasons, such a procedure is more concerned with setting aside money for replacing the equipment rather than with the economic values, to the company, of replacing it at specific times. D.P. provides a natural way of deducing such values which are derived from optimal future economic behaviour pre-requisites.

A fair amount of research into economic replacement intervals has been carried out previously by the Machinery and Allied Products Institute (M.A.P.I. for short) and later by Terborgh [45]. Although an effort is made to take account of the effect of present decisions on future decisions, and also to take account of technological changes, nevertheless these analyses are not based on the principle of optimizing long term economic behaviour. Bellman [4] is, to my knowledge, the first one to attempt to do so."

The application of the D.P. concept to maintenance problems is further illustrated in the following section and in Chapter 6.

4.5 Optimal replacement policy for two machines one of which acts as a standby, when the operating cost of a machine increases with use

4.5.1 STATEMENT OF PROBLEM

A production machine decreases in efficiency with use and this decrease can be measured by an increase in operating costs. To reduce operating costs a replacement can be made, at a cost. The production process is continuous and there is an installed standby machine. The problem is to determine an optimal combined replacement policy for the two, not necessarily identical, machines to minimize the total cost of replacement and operation over a fixed period of time.

This problem also takes into account the time required to effect a replacement (or, of course, it could be an overhaul of a major nature which can be considered to return the equipment to the as new condition, thus enabling us to use the term replacement).

4.5.2 CONSTRUCTION OF MODEL

(1) The state of the production system at the start of a period (say a week or a month) is denoted by I, where I is equivalent to two numbers (x, y) with x denoting the machine, A or B, which is currently being used and y referring to the age of the machine since it was last replaced.

(2) The operating cost for one period is $c_x(y)$.

(3) The state of the production system at the end of a period is J, where J is equivalent to two numbers (x, y), as defined above.

(4) The cost of replacement is C_r, which will be taken to be the same for both machines. (This is not necessary but it simplifies the calculations.)

(5) The time required to effect a replacement is one period. When the decision is taken to replace a machine production is switched to the standby.

(6) $C(I, J)$ is the total cost of starting with the system in state I at the beginning of a period and being in state J at the end.

(7) The objective is to determine a combined replacement/operation policy such that the total cost of replacement and operation over the next n periods of time is minimized.

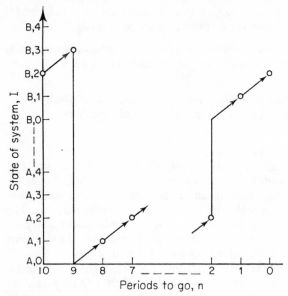

Fig. 4.17

Figure 4.17 illustrates the sort of policy that might occur if, with 10 periods to go, the system is in state $I = (B, 2)$, i.e. machine B has been used the previous period and is now of age 2 since last replacement.

At the start of the 10th period the decision is taken to continue with machine B.

At the start of the 9th period the decision is taken to replace machine B. This means that production is switched to machine A (which is assumed to be in a replaced condition) and at the end of the 9th period machine A is one period old, i.e. state $J = (A, 2)$.

At the start of the 8th period the decision is taken to continue with machine A; etc.

The model for this problem is constructed in exactly the same manner as in Section 4.4.2. The minimum total cost of replacement and operation, with n periods to go and starting in state I is $f_n(I)$. (Note that I refers to the state of the system and not to machine age as in Section 4.4.)

The cost of the first decision, i.e. the decision taken at the start of the nth period, is $C(I, J)$.

At the end of the period we are in state J, with $(n-1)$ periods to go. The minimum total cost over this remaining time is $f_{n-1}(J)$.

Thus, if as a result of our first decision we are in state J, with $(n-1)$ periods to go, the total cost is

$$C(I, J) + f_{n-1}(J)$$

Since we wish to minimize total cost we must take the decision at the start of the nth period so that we go to that value of J which minimizes total cost. Thus

$$f_n(I) = \frac{\min}{J} \, [C(I, J) + f_{n-1}(J)] \tag{4.8}$$

Equation (4.8) is the same as equation (4.7) of Section 4.4.2. The difference between the two models is that the state description I in each is different.

4.5.3 NUMERICAL EXAMPLE

(1) The trends in operating costs for two machines A and B are given in Table 4.10. Note that in both cases once a machine is of age 3 or greater the operating cost can be assumed to level-off and remain constant.

Table 4.10

Age of machine since last replaced, a	Machine A Operating cost for one period $c_A(a)(£)$	Machine B Operating cost for one period $c_B(a)(£)$
0	100	100
1	200	150
2	250	225
3 and over	300	250

(2) The cost of replacement for either machine, $C_r = £100$.
(3) The cost matrix for being in state I at the start of a period and finishing in stage J can be constructed as follows.

For each machine there are 4 possible states which can describe its condition; therefore there are 8 possible conditions at the start of a period, namely:

(x, y)	I	
$A, 0$	1	machine A new at start of period
$A, 1$	2	machine A of age 1 at start of period
$A, 2$	3	2
$A, 3$	4	3
$B, 0$	5	machine B new at start of period
$B, 1$	6	machine B of age 1 at start of period
$B, 2$	7	2
$B, 3$	8	3

The possible values of J which can occur at the end of a period can be easily identified since there are only two alternatives available at the start of a period: CONTINUE WITH SAME MACHINE or REPLACE AND USE STANDBY MACHINE. Thus the possible J values are as follows:

	I
$(A, 0)$	1
$(A, 1)$	2
$(A, 2)$	3
$(A, 3)$	4
$(B, 0)$	5
$(B, 1)$	6
$(B, 2)$	7
$(B, 3)$	8

	J	
		Where $J = 4$ corresponds to continuing with machine A and
$(A, 1)$ or $(B, 1)$	2 or 6	$J = 6$ corresponds to changing to machine B (which is assumed to be new at start of period)
$(A, 2)$ or $(B, 1)$	3 or 6	
$(A, 3)$ or $(B, 1)$	4 or 6	←sumed to be new at start of
$(A, 4) \equiv (A, 3)$ or $(B, 1)$	4 or 6	period)
$(B, 1)$ or $(A, 1)$	6 or 2	Where $J = 8$ corresponds to continuing with machine B and
$(B, 2)$ or $(A, 1)$	7 or 2	
$(B, 3)$ or $(A, 1)$	8 or 2	←$J = 2$ corresponds to changing
$(B, 4) \equiv (B, 3)$ or $(A, 1)$	8 or 2	to machine A (which is assumed to be new at start of period)

The cost matrix for being in state *I* at start of period and *J* at end is given in Table 4.11.

Table 4.11

$I \diagdown J$	1	2	3	4	5	6	7	8
1	∞	100	∞	∞	∞	100	∞	∞
2	∞	∞	200	∞	∞	200	∞	∞
3	∞	∞	∞	250	∞	200	∞	∞
4	∞	∞	∞	300	∞	200	∞	∞
5	∞	100	∞	∞	∞	100	∞	∞
6	∞	200	∞	∞	∞	∞	150	∞
7	∞	200	∞	∞	∞	∞	∞	225
8	∞	200	∞	∞	∞	∞	∞	250

An infinite cost is placed in the matrix when it is impossible to make a particular move.

The other costs in the matrix are obtained in a similar way to those of Section 4.4.3. For example if the state is $I = 2$ at the start of the period and the decision is taken to CONTINUE the cost is $C(2, 3) = c_A(2) = 200$. If the decision to change to machine *B* is taken the cost is

$$C(2, 6) = C_r + c_B(0) = 100 + 100 = £200$$

Note that it is assumed that whenever the decision is taken to change to the standby machine the first machine is replaced and, since it takes one period to replace the machine, it will then be the standby and in the as new state at the start of the next period when a decision has again to be taken. There are only two exceptions to this rule: the cost of going from state 1 to state 6, i.e. $C(1, 6)$ does not include a replacement cost for machine *A*, since it is already new, and $C(5, 2)$ does not include a replacement cost for machine *B* since it too is new.

(4) The problem is to determine the replacement policy to be adopted if, with 4 periods to go, we are in state $I = 6$, i.e. machine *B* is being used and is one period old, and machine *A* has been replaced and is in the as new condition.

Equation (4.8) is

$$f_n(I) = \min_J \; [C(I, J) + f_{n-1}(J)]$$

With 0 period to go, obviously,

$$f_0(I) = 0 \text{ for all possible values of } I$$

With 1 period to go,

$$f_1(I) = \genfrac{}{}{0pt}{}{\min}{J} [C(I, J) + f_0(J)]$$

$$= \genfrac{}{}{0pt}{}{\min}{J} [C(I, J)] \quad \text{since } f_0(J) = 0$$

If $I = 1$, at start of period,

$$f_1(1) = \min \begin{bmatrix} C(1, 1) \\ C(1, 2) \\ C(1, 3) \\ C(1, 4) \\ C(1, 5) \\ C(1, 6) \\ C(1, 7) \\ C(1, 8) \end{bmatrix} = \min \begin{bmatrix} \infty \\ 100 \\ \infty \\ \infty \\ \infty \\ 100 \\ \infty \\ \infty \end{bmatrix} \begin{matrix} \\ \leftarrow \text{min., i.e. CONTINUE} \\ \\ \\ \\ \leftarrow \text{min., i.e. REPLACE} \\ \\ \end{matrix}$$

Thus, with 1 period to go with $I = 1$, it does not matter whether we use machine A or change to machine B since the total cost in either case is £100.

Similarly, when $I = 2$, the minimum total cost of £200 occurs when $J = 3$ or 6 and it does not matter which decision is taken.

When $I = 3$,

$$f_1(3) = \min \begin{bmatrix} C(3, 1) \\ C(3, 2) \\ C(3, 3) \\ C(3, 4) \\ C(3, 5) \\ C(3, 6) \\ C(3, 7) \\ C(3, 8) \end{bmatrix} = \min \begin{bmatrix} \infty \\ \infty \\ \infty \\ 250 \\ \infty \\ 200 \\ \infty \\ \infty \end{bmatrix} \begin{matrix} \\ \\ \\ \\ \\ \leftarrow \text{min., i.e. CHANGE} \\ \\ \end{matrix}$$

Thus, with 1 period to go, the decision to take to minimize total cost is to change to machine B.

Table 4.12

I	1	2	3	4	5	6	7	8	
J	2 or 6	3 or 6	6	6	2 or 6	7	2	2	1 period to go
Action	C or R	C or R	R	R	R or C	C	R	R	
Cost $f_1(I)$	100	200	200	200	100	150	200	200	

R = REPLACE and change to standby
C = CONTINUE with same machine

Proceeding as above, Table 4.12 can be constructed which gives, for any condition I, and 1 period to go, the best state to be in at the end of the period, J, the associated minimum total cost $f_1(I)$, and the action to take.

Equation (4.8) can now be solved recursively when there are 2 periods to go:

$$f_2(I) = \frac{\min}{J} \; [C(I, J) + f_1(J)]$$

When $I = 1$,

$$f_2(1) = \min \begin{bmatrix} C(1, 1) + f_1(1) \\ C(1, 2) + f_1(2) \\ C(1, 3) + f_1(3) \\ C(1, 4) + f_1(4) \\ C(1, 5) + f_1(5) \\ C(1, 6) + f_1(6) \\ C(1, 7) + f_1(7) \\ C(1, 8) + f_1(8) \end{bmatrix}$$

$$= \min \begin{bmatrix} \infty & + & 100 \\ 100 & + & 200 \\ \infty & + & 200 \\ \infty & + & 200 \\ \infty & + & 100 \\ 100 & + & 150 \\ \infty & + & 200 \\ \infty & + & 200 \end{bmatrix} = \min \begin{bmatrix} \infty \\ 300 \\ \infty \\ \infty \\ \infty \\ 250 \\ \infty \\ \infty \end{bmatrix} \begin{matrix} \\ \\ \\ \\ \\ \leftarrow \text{min., i.e.} \\ \text{change to} \\ \text{machine } B \end{matrix}$$

In a similar way Table 4.13 can be obtained for other values of I with 2 periods to go.

Table 4.13

I	1	2	3	4	5	6	7	8	
J	6	6	6	6	6	7	2	2	2 periods
Action	R	R	R	R	C	C	R	R	to go
Cost $f_2(I)$	250	350	350	350	250	350	400	400	

Now that the $f_2(I)$ values are obtained, equation (4.8) can be solved to get the $f_3(I)$ values, and then the $f_4(I)$ values, and so on. The corresponding decisions for $f_3(I)$ and $f_4(I)$ are given in Tables 4.14 and 4.15.

Table 4.14

I	1	2	3	4	5	6	7	8	
J	2 or 6	3 or 6	6	6	2 or 6	2 or 7	2	2	3 periods to go
Action	C or R	C or R	R	R	R or C	R or C	R	R	
Cost $f_3(I)$	450	550	550	550	450	550	550	550	

Table 4.15

I	1	2	3	4	5	6	7	8	
J	2 or 6	3 or 6	6	6	2 or 6	7	2	2	4 periods to go
Action	C or R	C or R	R	R	R or C	C	R	R	
Cost $f_4(I)$	650	750	750	750	650	700	750	750	

Now that Tables 4.12 to 4.15 have been constructed it is possible to determine that the cost of the optimal replacement policy, starting in state $I = 6$ with 4 periods to go, is £700 (Table 4.15) and the decision rule is:

with 4 periods to go and $I = 6$:	Continue with machine B (then $J = 7$) (Table 4.15)
3 $I = 7$:	Replace machine B and use machine A (then $J = 2$) (Table 4.14)
2 $I = 2$:	Replace machine A and use machine B (then $J = 6$) (Table 4.13)
1 $I = 6$:	Continue with machine B (then $J = 7$) (Table 4.12)

4.5.4 FURTHER COMMENTS
Instead of having installed standby equipment it may be that production is continued using subcontractors or less efficient plant. When this is the case, an approach similar to that of the above example can be adopted where the costs of using the alternative methods are used in the model instead of the operating costs of the installed standby.

4.6 Optimal replacement interval for capital equipment: maximization of discounted benefits

4.6.1 STATEMENT OF PROBLEM

Through use, equipment deteriorates and this deterioration may be measured by the net benefit derived from operating the equipment. Eventually the net benefit will reach a stage where it becomes economically justifiable to replace the equipment. What we wish to determine is an optimal replacement policy which maximizes the total discounted net benefits derived from operating the equipment over a long period. It will be assumed that equipment is replaced by identical equipment, thus returning the equipment to the as new condition after replacement. Further, it is assumed that the trends in cost and benefit following each replacement will remain identical. Since the equipment is being operated over a long period the replacement policy will be periodic and so we will determine the optimal replacement interval.

4.6.2 CONSTRUCTION OF MODEL

(1) $b(t)$ is the net benefit obtained from the equipment at time t. This will be the revenue derived from operating the equipment minus the operating costs which may include maintenance costs, fuel costs, etc. A possible form of $b(t)$ is illustrated in Figure 4.18.

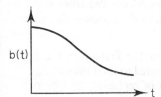

Fig. 4.18

(2) $c(t)$ is the net cost of replacing equipment of age t. Replacing the equipment includes the purchase price plus installation cost and may also include a cost for loss of production due to the time required to replace the equipment. These costs are often partially offset by the salvage value of the used equipment, which usually depends on the age of the equipment when it is replaced. A possible form of $c(t)$ is illustrated in Figure 4.19.

(3) T_r is the time required to replace the equipment.

(4) t_r is the age of the equipment when replacement occurs.

(5) $t_r + T_r$ is the replacement cycle. That is, the time from the finish of one replacement action to the next.

(6) $B(t_r)$ is the total discounted net benefits derived from operating the equipment for periods of length t_r, over a long time.

(7) The objective is to determine the optimum interval between replacements to maximize the total discounted net benefits derived from operating the equipment over a long period of time.

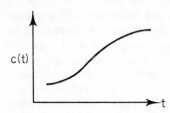

Fig. 4.19

$B(t_r) =$ Sum of the discounted net benefits from each replacement cycle over a long period of time. For purposes of the analysis the period over which replacements will occur will be taken as infinity, although in practice this will not be the case.

Consider the first cycle of operation

Defining $B_1(t_r + T_r)$ as the total net benefits derived from replacing the equipment at age t_r, discounted back to their present day value at the start of the first cycle we get:

$B_1(t_r + T_r) =$ Benefits received over the first cycle, i.e. in interval $(0, t_r)$ discounted to their present day value *minus* the cost of replacing equipment of age t_r, discounted to its present day value

This first cycle of operation is illustrated in Figure 4.20.

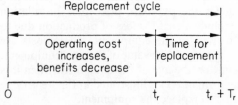

Fig. 4.20

Discounted benefits over first cycle $= \int_0^{t_r} b(t) \exp\left[-it\right] dt$

where i is the relevant interest rate.

Discounted replacement cost $= c(t_r) \exp\left[-it_r\right]$

$$B_1(t_r + T_r) = \int_0^{t_r} b(t) \exp\left[-it\right] dt - c(t_r) \exp\left[-it_r\right]$$

Consider the second cycle of operation
Defining $B_2(t_r + T_r)$ as the total net benefits derived from replacing the equipment at age t_r discounted back to their present day value at the start of the second cycle we get:

$$B_2(t_r + T_r) = \int_0^{t_r} b(t) \exp\left[-it\right] dt - c(t_r) \exp\left[-it_r\right]$$

What we now want to do is discount $B_2(t_r + T_r)$ back to the start of the first cycle and this is

$$B_2(t_r + T_r) \exp\left[-i(t_r + T_r)\right]$$

Consider the third cycle of operation
Defining $B_3(t_r + T_r)$ as the total net benefits derived from replacing the equipment at age t_r, discounted back to give their present day value at the start of the third cycle we get:

$$B_3(t_r + T_r) = \int_0^{t_r} b(t) \exp\left[-it\right] dt - c(t_r) \exp\left[-it_r\right]$$

Discounting $B_3(t_r + T_r)$ back to the start of the first replacement cycle:

$$B_3(t_r + T_r) \exp\left[-i2(t_r + T_r)\right]$$

Consider the nth cycle of operation
Defining $B_n(t_r + T_r)$ similar to the others we get:

$$B_n(t_r + T_r) = \int_0^{t_r} b(t) \exp\left[-it\right] dt - c(t_r) \exp\left[-it_r\right]$$

which discounted back to the start of the first cycle gives

$$B_n(t_r + T_r) \exp\left[-i(n - 1)(t_r + T_r)\right]$$

The form which the benefits take over the first few cycles of operation are illustrated in Figure 4.21.

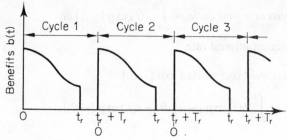

Fig. 4.21

Thus the total discounted net benefit, over a long period of time, with replacement at age t_r, is

$$B(t_r) = B_1(t_r + T_r) + B_2(t_r + T_r) \exp\left[-i(t_r + T_r)\right]$$
$$+ B_3(t_r + T_r) \exp\left[-i2(t_r + T_r)\right]$$
$$+ \ldots + B_n(t_r + T_r) \exp\left[-i(n-1)(t_r + T_r)\right] + \ldots$$

Since $B_1(t_r + T_r) = B_2(t_r + T_r) = B_3(t_r + T_r) = \ldots = B_n(t_r + T_r)$ $= \ldots$, we can write

$$B(t_r) = B_1(t_r + T_r) + B_1(t_r + T_r) \exp\left[-i(t_r + T_r)\right]$$
$$+ B_1(t_r + T_r) \exp\left[-i2(t_r + T_r)\right]$$
$$+ \ldots + B_1(t_r + T_r) \exp\left[-i(n-1)(t_r + T_r)\right] + \ldots$$
$$(4.9)$$

Equation (4.9) is a geometric progression to infinity which gives

$$B(t_r) = \frac{B_1(t_r + T_r)}{1 - \exp\left[-i(t_r + T_r)\right]}$$

i.e.

$$B(t_r) = \frac{\int_0^{t_r} b(t) \exp\left[-it\right] dt - c(t_r) \exp\left[-it_r\right]}{1 - \exp\left[-i(t_r + T_r)\right]} \qquad (4.10)$$

This is a model of the replacement problem relating the replacement age t_r to the total discounted net benefits.

Rather than summing the progression to infinity we could sum the first n terms which gives (see section 3.2 for formula):

$$B(t_r) = \left(\int_0^{t_r} b(t) \exp\left[-it\right] dt - c(t_r) \exp\left[-it_r\right] \right)$$
$$\times \left(\frac{1 - \exp\left[-ni(t_r + T_r)\right]}{1 - \exp\left[-i(t_r + T_r)\right]} \right)$$

which results in the same optimal value of t_r as would be obtained from equation (4.10) since the top term in the second bracket is a constant (see proof of section 4.6.5), although the benefit $B(t_r)$ would be reduced by this factor.

4.6.3 NUMERICAL EXAMPLE

The benefits derived from operating equipment are of the form

$b(t) = £32\,000 \exp[-0.09t]$ per year
Cost of replacement $c(t) = £(150000 - 13600 \exp[-0.73t])$

The time required to perform a replacement is one month. Determine the optimal replacement age of the equipment when i is taken as 10%.

Equation (4.10) becomes

$$B(t_r) = \frac{\displaystyle\int_0^{t_r} 32000 \exp[-0.09t] \exp[-0.1t]\,dt}{1 - \exp[-0.1(t_r + 0.083)]} \qquad (4.11)$$

$$-(15000 - 13600 \exp[-0.73t_r]) \exp[-0.1t_r]$$

Now

$$\int_0^{t_r} 32000 \exp[-0.09t] \exp[-0.1t]\,dt = \int_0^{t_r} 32000 \exp[-0.19t]\,dt$$

$$= \left[\frac{-32000}{0.19} \exp[-0.19t]\right]_0^{t_r} = 168\,421(1 - \exp[-0.19t_r])$$

Therefore

$$B(t_r) = \frac{\begin{array}{c}168\,421(1 - \exp[-0.19t_r]) \\ -(15000 - 13600 \exp[-0.73t_r]) \exp[-0.1t_r]\end{array}}{1 - \exp[-0.1(t_r + 0.083)]} \qquad (4.12)$$

Evaluating equation (4.12) for various values of t_r gives Table 4.16. From the table it is clear that the benefits are maximized when replacement occurs at the end of the fourth year of operation.

Table 4.16

t_r	1	2	3	4	5	6	7	8
$B(t_r)(\times 10^3)$	210	232	238	239	236	232	229	225

4.6.4 FURTHER COMMENTS

In the model for capital equipment replacement no consideration was given to tax allowances which may be available. This is an aspect which is rarely mentioned in replacement studies but which must be included where relevant. One paper which extends the model discussed here to consider problems of tax is that of Eilon *et al.* [17].

Also, in the example the time required to effect replacement has been included in the analysis. In practice this time can usually be omitted since it is often small compared to the interval between replacements and so does not make any noticeable difference to the optimal replacement interval whether it is included or not.

It may seem unreasonable that we should sum the terms of the geometric progression to infinity. This, however, does make the calculations a little easier and gives an indication of the sort of interval we would expect to have between replacements. The dynamic programming approach of Sections 4.4 and 4.5 can be applied equally well to capital replacement problems (see, for example, [48]). The difficulty is, of course, to decide whether the more sophisticated analysis, which costs more to carry out, is likely to give a solution which is a significant improvement over the solution obtained the "easy way".

4.6.5 PROOF THAT OPTIMIZATION OVER A LONG PERIOD IS NOT EQUIVALENT TO OPTIMIZATION PER UNIT TIME WHEN DISCOUNTING IS INCLUDED

When dealing with long-term decisions, such as replacement of capital equipment, where the time value of money is taken into account, it is necessary to determine the replacement policy to maximize the performance measure (such as profit, cost, benefit, etc.) over the long period and not maximize performance per unit time as is the case when dealing with short-term decisions.

The basic problem is illustrated in Figure 4.22, where

    T period of time over which we wish to optimize
    t_r interval between replacements which we wish to determine such that they are optimum

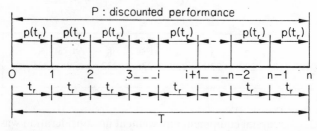

Fig. 4.22

$p(t_r)$ performance over one interval, which is dependent upon interval length t_r and assumed identical for each period of length t_r

P total discounted performance over period T which we wish to optimize (we will assume we wish to maximize P)

n number of replacement intervals in period $(0, T)$

$$\max(P) = \max \left[p(t_r) + p(t_r) \exp[-it_r] + p(t_r) \exp[-2it_r] \right.$$
$$\left. + \ldots + p(t_r) \exp[-(n-1)it_r] \right]$$
$$= \max \left[\left(\frac{1 - \exp[-nit_r]}{1 - \exp[it_r]} \right) p(t_r) \right]$$
$$= \max \left[\left(\frac{1 - \exp[-iT]}{1 - \exp[-it_r]} \right) p(t_r) \right]$$

Now $(1 - \exp[-iT])$ is constant, and therefore

$$\max(P) \equiv \max \left[\frac{p(t_r)}{1 - \exp[-it_r]} \right]$$

and not $p(t_r)/t_r$ which would be the result if discounting were neglected.

4.7 Optimal replacement interval for capital equipment: minimization of total cost

4.7.1 STATEMENT OF PROBLEM

This problem is similar to that of Section 4.6 except that: (*a*) the objective is to determine the replacement interval that minimizes the total cost of maintenance and replacement over a long period; and (*b*) the trend in costs is taken to be discrete, rather than continuous.

4.7.2 CONSTRUCTION OF MODEL

(1) A is the acquisition cost of the capital equipment.

(2) C_i is the cost of maintenance in the ith period from new, assumed to be paid at the end of the period, $i = 1, 2 \ldots, n$.

(3) S_i is the resale value of the equipment at the end of the ith period of operation $i = 1, 2, \ldots, n$.

(4) r is the discount rate.

(5) n is the age in periods of the equipment when replaced.

(6) $C(n)$ is the total discounted cost of maintaining and replacing the equipment (with identical equipment) over a long period of time with replacements occurring at intervals of n periods.

(7) The objective is to determine the optimal interval between replacements to minimize total discounted costs, $C(n)$.

The replacement policy is illustrated in Figure 4.23.

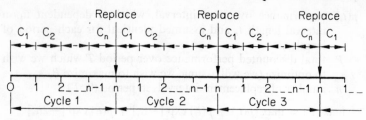

Fig. 4.23

Consider first cycle of operation
Total cost over first cycle of operation, with equipment already installed is

$$C_1(n) = C_1 r + C_2 r^2 + C_3 r^3 + \ldots + C_n r^n + A r^n - S_n r^n$$
$$= \sum_{i=1}^{n} C_i r^i + r^n(A - S_n)$$

For the second cycle, the total cost discounted to the start of the second cycle is

$$C_2(n) = \sum_{i=1}^{n} C_i r^i + r^n(A - S_n)$$

Similarly, the total costs of the third, fourth, etc., cycle, discounted back to the start of their cycle, can be obtained.

The total discounted costs, when discounting is taken to the start of the operation, i.e. at time 0, is

$$C(n) = C_1(n) + C_2(n)r^n + C_3(n)r^{2n} + \ldots + C_n(n)r^{(n-1)n}$$
$$+ \ldots$$

Since $C_1(n) = C_2(n) = C_3(n) = \ldots = C_n(n) = \ldots$, we have a geometric progression which gives, over an infinite period:

$$C(n) = \frac{C_1(n)}{1 - r^n} = \frac{\sum_{i=1}^{n} C_i r^i + r^n(A - S_n)}{1 - r^n} \tag{4.13}$$

This is a model of the problem relating replacement interval n to total costs.

4.7.3 NUMERICAL EXAMPLE
  (1) Let $A = £5000$.
  (2) The estimated maintenance costs per year for the next 5 years are in Table 4.17.

Table 4.17

Year	1	2	3	4	5
Estimated maintenance cost £	500	1 000	2 000	3 000	4 000

(3) The estimated resale values over the next 5 years are in Table 4.18.

Table 4.18

Year	1	2	3	4	5
Resale value £	3 000	2 000	1 000	750	500

(4) The discount rate $r = 0.9$.

Evaluation of equation (4.13) for different values of n gives the figures of Table 4.19 from which it is seen that the best time to replace (i.e. the "economic life" of the equipment) is after the equipment has been used for two years.

Table 4.19

Replacement time (n)	1	2	3	4	5
Total discounted costs $C(n)$	22 500	19 421	20 790	21 735	23 701

Sample calculation
When $n = 2$, equation (4.13) becomes

$$C(2) = \frac{500(0.9) + 1\,000(0.9)^2 + (0.9)^2(5\,000 - 2\,000)}{1 - 0.9^2}$$

$$= £19\,421 \text{ per year}$$

4.7.4 FURTHER COMMENTS

In the example it has been assumed that the acquisition cost of equipment could be taken as remaining constant. Also it was assumed that the trend in maintenance costs was the same after each replacement. Because of inflationary trends this is unlikely and, therefore, it may be necessary to modify the model to take account of these facts.

Note, however, that the interest rate used when calculating the discount rate is unlikely to be the same as the inflation rate, and so they do not cancel each other out. For example, inflation may occur at 6% per annum, whereas the interest rate appropriate for discounting purposes may be something like 25%, giving $r = 0.8$.

In practice, of course, new equipment comes on the market and we do not always replace equipment with identical equipment. Thus, as time goes on we need to repeat our calculations using, when appropriate, new cost figures and so check whether it is necessary to modify the replacement interval.

The example of the following section gives an indication of how technological improvement can be incorporated into a model.

4.8 Optimal replacement policy for capital equipment taking into account technological improvement: finite planning horizon

4.8.1 STATEMENT OF PROBLEM

When determining a replacement policy there may be on the market equipment which is, in some way, a technological improvement on the equipment currently used. For example maintenance and operating costs may be lower, throughput may be greater, quality of output may be better, etc. The problem discussed in this section is how to determine when, if at all, to take advantage of the technologically improved equipment.

It will be assumed that there is a fixed period of time from now during which equipment will be required and, if replacement is with the new equipment, then this equipment will remain in use until the end of the fixed period. The objective will be to determine when to make the replacement, if at all, to minimize total discounted costs of maintenance and replacement.

4.8.2 CONSTRUCTION OF MODEL

(1) n is the number of operating periods during which equipment will be required.

(2) $C_{p,i}$ is the maintenance cost of the present equipment in the ith period from now, payable at time i, $i = 1, 2, \ldots, n$.

(3) $S_{p,i}$ is the resale value of the present equipment at the end of the ith period from now, $i = 0, 1, 2 \ldots, n$.

(4) A is the acquisition cost of the technologically improved equipment.

(5) $C_{t,j}$ is the maintenance cost of the technologically improved equipment in the jth period after its installation and payable at time j, $j = 1, 2, \ldots, n$.

(6) $S_{t,j}$ is the resale value of the technologically improved equipment at the end of its jth period of operation $j = 0, 1, 2 . . ., n$. ($j = 0$ is included so that we can then define $S_{t,0} = A$. This then enables Ar^n in the model (see equation 4.14) to be cancelled if no change is made.)

Note that it is assumed that if a replacement is to be made at all then it is with the technologically improved equipment. This is not unreasonable since it may be that the equipment currently in use is no longer on the market.

(7) r is the discount factor.

(8) The objective is to determine that value of T, at which replacement should take place, with the new equipment, $T = 0, 1, 2, . . ., n$. The policy is illustrated in Figure 4.24.

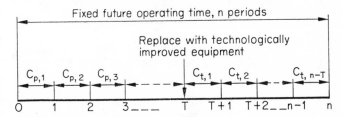

Fig. 4.24

Total discounted cost over n periods, with replacement occurring at the end of the Tth period is

$C(T) =$ Discounted maintenance costs for present equipment over period $(0, T)$
+ Discounted maintenance costs for technologically improved equipment over period (T, n)
+ Discounted acquisition cost of new equipment
− Discounted resale value of present equipment at end of Tth period
− Discounted resale value of technologically improved equipment at end of nth period

$$= (C_{p,1}r^1 + C_{p,2}r^2 + C_{p,3}r^3 + . . . + C_{p,T}r^T)$$
$$+ (C_{t,1}r^{T+1} + C_{t,2}r^{T+2} + . . . + C_{t,n-T}r^n) + Ar^T$$
$$- (S_{p,T}r^T + S_{t,n-T}r^n)$$

Therefore

$$C(T) = \sum_{i=1}^{T} C_{p,i}r^i + \sum_{j=1}^{n-T} C_{t,j}r^{T+j} + Ar^T - (S_{p,T}r^T + S_{t,n-T}r^n)$$

$$(4.14)$$

This is a model of the problem relating replacement time T to total discounted costs $C(T)$.

4.8.3 NUMERICAL EXAMPLE

(1) The number of operating periods still to go, $n = 6$.
(2) The estimated maintenance costs $C_{p,i}$ over the next 6 periods of the present equipment are shown in Table 4.20.

Table 4.20

Period (i)	1	2	3	4	5	6
Maintenance cost $C_{p,i}$(£)	5000	6 000	7000	7500	8000	8500

(3) The estimated trend in resale values of the present equipment payable at the end of the period is shown in Table 4.21.

Table 4.21

Period (i)	0 (i.e. now)	1	2	3	4	5	6
Resale value $S_{p,i}$(£)	3000	2000	1000	500	500	500	500

(4) The acquisition cost of the technologically improved equipment is $A = £10000$.
(5) The estimated maintenance costs $C_{t,j}$ over the next 6 periods of the technologically improved equipment are in Table 4.22.

Table 4.22

Period (j)	1	2	3	4	5	6
Maintenance cost $C_{t,j}$(£)	100	200	500	750	1000	1200

(6) The estimated trend in resale value of the technologically improved equipment, payable at the end of its jth period, of operation $S_{t,j}$ is in Table 4.23.

Table 4.23

Period (j)	0	1	2	3	4	5	6
Resale value $S_{t,j}$(£)	10000	8000	7000	6000	5000	4500	4000

(7) The discount rate $r = 0.9$.

Evaluation of equation (4.14) for different values of T gives Table 4.24 from which it is seen that the total costs are minimized when $T = 0$, i.e. the technologically improved equipment should be installed now and used over the next 6 periods of operation.

Table 4.24

Replacement time, T	0	1	2	3	4	5	6
Total discounted costs, $C(T)$	7211	10836	14891	18649	22062	25519	28359

Note that if the minimum total cost occurs at $T = n$ (6 in this example) this would mean that no replacement would take place and the present equipment would be used for the remaining n periods of operation. If the minimum value of $C(T)$ occurs for a value of T between 0 and n then the replacement should occur with the technologically improved equipment at the end of the Tth period.

Sample calculation
When $T = 3$, i.e.

$$\text{Replace} \downarrow$$

$$\underset{0 \quad 1 \quad 2 \quad T = 3 \quad 4 \quad 5 \quad 6}{\underbrace{\qquad\qquad\qquad\qquad\qquad\qquad\qquad}}$$

$$C(3) = C_{p,1}r^1 + C_{p,2}r^2 + C_{p,3}r^3 + Ar^3 + C_{t,1}r^4 + C_{t,2}r^5 + C_{t,3}r^6$$
$$\qquad - (S_{p,3}r^3 + S_{t,3}r^6)$$
$$= 5000(0.9) + 6000(0.9)^2 + 7000(0.9)^3 + 10000(0.9)^3 +$$
$$\qquad 100(0.9)^4 + 200(0.9)^5 + 500(0.9)^6 - [500(0.9)^3 + 6000(0.9)^6]$$
$$= £18\,649$$

4.8.4 FURTHER COMMENTS

The example in this section assumed that, once the decision was
taken to replace with the technologically improved equipment, no
further replacements were made. In some situations the time during
which equipment is required is sufficiently long to warrant further
replacements. Assuming that we continue to use the technologically
improved equipment then it is not difficult to determine its economic
life. Such a problem is covered in the following section.

4.9 Optimal replacement policy for capital equipment taking into account technological improvement: infinite planning horizon

4.9.1 STATEMENT OF PROBLEM

The statement of this replacement problem is virtually identical to
that of Section 4.8.1 except that once the decision has been taken to
replace with the technologically improved equipment then this
equipment will continue to be used and a replacement policy (periodic)
will be required for it. It will be assumed that replacement will continue to be made with the technologically improved equipment. Again
we wish to determine the policy that minimizes total discounted costs
of maintenance and replacement.

4.9.2 CONSTRUCTION OF MODEL

(1) $C_{p,i}$, $S_{p,i}$, A, $C_{t,j}$, $S_{t,j}$, r are as defined in Section 4.8.2.
(2) The replacement policy is illustrated in Figure 4.25.

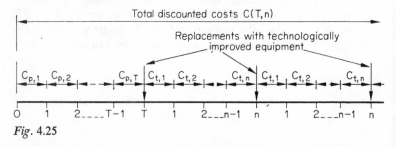

Fig. 4.25

The total discounted cost over a long period of time with replacement of the present equipment at the end of T periods of operation,
followed by replacements of the technologically improved equipment
at intervals of n, is

$$C(T, n) = \text{Costs over interval } (0, T) + \text{Future costs}$$

$$\textit{Costs over interval } (0, T) = \sum_{i=1}^{T} C_{p,i}r^i - S_{p,T}r^T + Ar^T$$

Future costs, discounted to time T, can be obtained by the method described in Section 4.7.2 (equation 4.13) where the economic life of equipment is calculated. We replace C_i by $C_{t,j}$ to obtain

$$C(n) = \frac{\sum\limits_{j=1}^{n} C_{t,j}r^j + r^n(A - S_n)}{1 - r^n} \qquad (4.15)$$

Therefore, $C(n)$ discounted to time zero is $C(n)r^T$ and

$$C(T, n) = \sum_{i=1}^{T} C_{p,i}r^i - S_{p,T}r^T + Ar^T + \left(\frac{\sum\limits_{j=1}^{n} C_{t,j}r^j + r^n(A - S_n)}{1 - r^n}\right)r^T \qquad (4.16)$$

This is a model of the problem relating changeover time to technologically improved equipment, T, and economic life of new equipment, n, to total discounted costs $C(T, n)$.

4.9.3 NUMERICAL EXAMPLE
Using the data of the example of Section 4.8.3 (4, 5, 6 and 7) we can determine the economic life of the technologically improved equipment and the value of $C(n)$ of equation (4.15). The data of Section 4.8.3 gives Table 4.26 from which it is seen that the economic life is five years and the corresponding value of $C(n)$ is £11 920.

Table 4.25

Replacement interval n	1	2	3	4	5	6
Total discounted costs $C(n)$	18 900	14 116	13 035	12 834	11 920	12 063

Insertion of $C(n) = $ £11 920 and $A = $ £10 000 into equation (4.16) gives

$$C(T, 5) = \sum_{i=1}^{T} C_{p,i}r^i - S_{p,T}r^T + 10\,000\,r^T + 11\,920\,r^T$$

$$= \sum_{i=1}^{T} C_{p,i}\,r^i - S_{p,T}r^T + 21\,920\,r^T \qquad (4.17)$$

Given the information of Tables 4.26 and 4.27 for the maintenance costs and resale prices for the present equipment, Table 4.28 can be obtained by inserting values of $T = 0, 1, 2, 3$ into equation (4.17). Thus it is seen that the present equipment should be used for one further year and then replaced with the technologically improved equipment, which should itself then be replaced at intervals of five years.

Table 4.26

Period (i)	1	2	3
Maintenance cost $C_{p,i}$(£)	1500	3000	4000

Table 4.27

Period (i)	0 (i.e. now)	1	2	3
Resale value $S_{p,i}$(£)	2750	2500	1500	1000

Table 4.28

Replacement time T	0	1	2	3
Total discounted costs $C(T, 5)$	19170	18828	20120	20946

Sample calculation
When $n = 3$, then equation (4.15) becomes

$$C(3) = \frac{100(0 \cdot 9) + 200(0 \cdot 9)^2 + 500(0 \cdot 9)^3 + (0 \cdot 9)^3(10000 - 6000)}{1 - (0 \cdot 9)^3}$$

$$= £13035$$

When $T = 2$, then equation (4.17) becomes

$$C(2, 5) = 1500(0 \cdot 9) + 3000(0 \cdot 9)^2 - 1500(0 \cdot 9)^2 + 21920(0 \cdot 9)^2$$

$$= £20120$$

4.9.4 FURTHER COMMENTS
Of course, technological improvement is occurring continuously and so perhaps we should cater for this in any model used for capital

replacement. The real problem here is not construction of the model but estimating the trends resulting from technological improvement. On the assumption of exponential trends in benefits, operation and replacement costs, Bellman and Dreyfus [5] construct a dynamic programming model which can be used to cater for technological improvement. Bellman and Dreyfus then extend the model to include the possibility of replacing with secondhand rather than new equipment. White [48] also discusses technological improvement in the context of replacement problems.

4.10 Optimal interval between preventive replacements of equipment subject to breakdown

4.10.1 STATEMENT OF PROBLEM

Equipment is subject to sudden failure and when failure occurs the equipment has to be replaced. Since failure is unexpected it is not unreasonable to assume that a failure replacement is more costly than a preventive replacement. For example, a preventive replacement is planned and arrangements are made to perform it without unnecessary delays, or perhaps a failure may cause damage to other equipment. In order to reduce the number of failures preventive replacements can be scheduled to occur at specified intervals. However, a balance is required between the amount spent on the preventive replacements and their resulting benefits, i.e. reduced failure replacements.

In this section it will be assumed, not unreasonably, that we are dealing with a long period of time over which the equipment is to be operated and the intervals between the preventive replacements are relatively short. When this is the case we need consider only one cycle of operations and develop a model for the cycle. If the interval between the preventive replacements was "long" it would be necessary to use the discounting approach and the series of cycles would have to be included in the model (see Section 4.6.5).

The replacement policy is one where preventive replacements occur at fixed intervals of time, and failure replacements occur when necessary, and we want to determine the optimal interval between the preventive replacements to minimize the total expected cost of replacing the equipment per unit time.

4.10.2 CONSTRUCTION MODEL

(1) C_p is the cost of a preventive replacement.
(2) C_f is the cost of a failure replacement.
(3) $f(t)$ is the probability density function of the equipment's failure times.

(4) The replacement policy is to perform preventive replacements at constant intervals of length t_p, irrespective of the age of the equipment, and failure replacements occur as many times as required in interval $(0, t_p)$. The policy is illustrated in Figure 4.26.

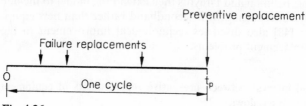

Fig. 4.26

(5) The objective is to determine the optimal interval between preventive replacements to minimize the total expected replacement cost per unit time.

The total expected cost per unit time, for preventive replacement at time t_p, denoted $C(t_p)$ is

$$C(t_p) = \frac{\text{Total expected cost in interval } (0, t_p)}{\text{Length of interval}}$$

Total expected cost = Cost of a preventive replacement
in interval $(0, t_p)$ $\qquad$ + Expected cost of failure replacements
$\qquad\qquad\qquad\quad = C_p + C_f H(t_p)$

where $H(t_p)$ is the expected number of failures in interval $(0, t_p)$.

Length of interval $= t_p$

Therefore

$$C(t_p) = \frac{C_p + C_f H(t_p)}{t_p} \tag{4.18}$$

This is a model of the problem relating replacement interval t_p to total cost $C(t_p)$.

A numerical solution to equation (4.18) will be illustrated by an example in Section 4.10.4. Before proceeding with the example we will illustrate how $H(t_p)$, the expected number of failures in an interval of length t_p, can be obtained.

4.10.3 DETERMINATION OF $H(t)$
Renewal theory approach
With reference to Figure 4.27 we may define the following terms:

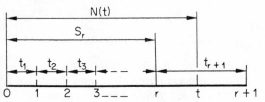

Fig. 4.27

$N(t)$ number of failures in interval $(0, t)$

$H(t)$ expected number of failures in interval $(0, t) = E[N(t)]$
where $E [\ ]$ denotes expectation.

t_1, t_2 intervals between failures

S_r time up to the rth failure $= t_1 + t_2 + \ldots + t_r$.

Now the probability of $N(t) = r$ is the probability that t lies between the rth and $(r + 1)$th failure. This is obtained as follows:

$$P[N(t) < r] = 1 - F_r(t)$$

where $F_r(t)$ is the cumulative distribution function of S_r.

$$P[N(t) > r] = F_{r+1}(t)$$

Now

$$P[N(t) < r] + P[N(t) = r] + P[N(t) > r] = 1$$

Therefore

$$P[N(t) = r] = F_r(t) - F_{r+1}(t)$$

The expected value of $N(t)$ is then

$$H(t) = \sum_{r=0}^{\infty} rP[N(t) = r] = \sum_{r=0}^{\infty} r[F_r(t) - F_{r+1}(t)]$$

$$H(t) = \sum_{r=1}^{\infty} F_r(t) \tag{4.19}$$

On taking Laplace transforms† of both sides of equation (4.19) we

† If the $f(t)$ is the probability density function of a non-negative random variable T, the Laplace transform $f^*(s)$ is defined by:

$$f^*(s) = E \exp [-sT] = \int_0^{\infty} \exp [-sT] f(t) \, dt$$

The main importance of Laplace transforms in renewal theory is in connection with the sums of independent random variables. For further details of renewal theory, see Cox [12].

get

$$H^*(s) = \frac{f^*(s)}{s[1 - f^*(s)]} \tag{4.20}$$

The problem is then to determine $H(t)$ from $H^*(s)$. This is done by determining $f(t)$ from $f^*(s)$, a process termed inversion. Inversion is usually done by reference to tables giving Laplace transforms of common functions and giving $f(t)$ corresponding to common forms of $f^*(s)$.

Example
If $f(t) = \lambda e^{-\lambda t}$ then from tables $F^*(s) = \lambda/(\lambda + s)$. From equation (4.20),

$$H^*(s) = \frac{\lambda/(\lambda + s)}{s[1 - \lambda/(\lambda + s)]} = \lambda/s^2$$

From tables the function corresponding to $1/s^2$ is t and so

$$H(t) = \lambda t$$

In practice $H^*(s)$ can only be inverted in simple cases. However, if t is large (tending to infinity),

$$H(t) = \frac{t}{\mu} + \frac{\sigma^2 - \mu^2}{2\mu^2} \tag{4.21}$$

where μ and σ^2 are the mean and variance of $f(t)$.

Example
Equipment fails according to the normal distribution with $\mu = 5$, $\sigma^2 = 1$. If the interval between preventive replacements is $t = 1\,000$ weeks, then from equation (4.21),

$$H(1\,000) = \frac{1\,000}{5} + \frac{1 - 25}{50} = 199 \cdot 5 \text{ failures}$$

Of course, we do not expect to get large numbers of failures between preventive replacements (if we do we are not doing preventive replacement) and so equation (4.21) is not appropriate and therefore we would need to use equation (4.20). Owing to possible difficulties of inverting $H^*(s)$ a "discrete" approach is usually adopted to determine $H(t)$. One possible approach which avoids this possible difficulty is as follows.

Discrete approach
Figure 4.28 illustrates the case where there are four weeks between preventive replacements. Then $H(4)$ is the expected number of failures in interval $(0, 4)$, starting with new equipment.

Fig. 4.28

When we start at time zero the first failure (if there is one) will occur either during the first, second, third or fourth week of operation. Keeping this fact in mind we get:

$H(4) =$ Number of expected failures which occur in interval $(0, 4)$ when the first failure occurs in the first week
× Probability of the first failure occurring in interval $(0, 1)$

+ Number of expected failures which occur in interval $(0, 4)$ when the first failure occurs in the second week
× Probability of the first failure occurring in interval $(1, 2)$

+ Number of expected failures which occur in interval $(0, 4)$ when the first failure occurs in the third week
× Probability of the first failure occurring in interval $(2, 3)$

+ Number of expected failures which occur in interval $(0, 4)$ when the first failure occurs in the fourth week
× Probability of the first failure occurring in interval $(3, 4)$.

Assume that not more than one failure can occur in any weekly interval. This is not restrictive since the length of each interval can be made as short as desired. If this is the case then:

Number of expected failures   The failure which occurred
which occur in interval $(0, 4)$ = in the first week + The
when the first failure occurs   expected number of failures
in the first week   in the remaining three weeks
$$= 1 + H(3)$$

Note we use $H(3)$ since we have new equipment as a result of replacing the failure in the first week and we then have three weeks to go before the preventive replacement occurs. By definition, the expected number of failures in the remaining three weeks, starting with the new equipment is $H(3)$.

Probability of the first failure occurring $= \int_0^1 f(t) \, dt$
in the first week

Similarly for consequences of the first failure occurring in the second, third and fourth weeks,

$$H(4) = [1 + H(3)] \int_0^1 f(t) \, dt + [1 + H(2)] \int_1^2 f(t) \, dt$$

$$+ [1 + H(1)] \int_2^3 f(t) \, dt + [1 + H(0)] \int_3^4 f(t) \, dt$$

Obviously, $H(0) = 0$. That is with zero weeks to go the expected number of failures is zero.

Tidying up the above equation we get

$$H(4) = \sum_{i=0}^3 [1 + H(3 - i)] \int_i^{i+1} f(t) \, dt$$

with $H(0) = 0$.

In general

$$H(T) = \sum_{i=0}^{T-1} [1 + H(T - i - 1)] \int_i^{i+1} f(t) \, dt \quad T \geqslant 1 \qquad (4.22)$$

with $H(0) = 0$

Equation (4.22) is termed a recurrence relation. Since we know that $H(0) = 0$, we can get $H(1)$, then $H(2)$, then $H(3)$, etc., from equation (4.22).

Example

Assume $f(t) = \frac{1}{6}$, $0 \leqslant t \leqslant 6$. This is illustrated in Figure 4.29 which is termed a uniform or rectangular distribution. Determine the expected number of failures if preventive replacements occur every two weeks.

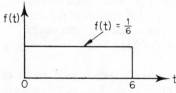

Fig. 4.29

In this case we want $H(2)$. From equation (4.22),

$$H(2) = \sum_{i=0}^{1} [1 + H(1 - i)] \int_{i}^{i+1} f(t)\, dt$$

$$= [1 + H(1)] \int_{0}^{1} f(t)\, dt + [1 + H(0)] \int_{1}^{2} f(t)\, dt$$

Now

$$H(0) = 0$$

$$H(1) = [1 + H(0)] \int_{0}^{1} f(t)\, dt \qquad \text{from equation (4.22)}$$

$$= \int_{0}^{1} \frac{1}{6}\, dt = \frac{1}{6}$$

$$H(2) = \left(1 + \frac{1}{6}\right) \int_{0}^{1} \frac{1}{6}\, dt + (1 + 0) \int_{1}^{2} \frac{1}{6}\, dt$$

$$= \frac{7}{6} \times \frac{1}{6} + 1 \times \frac{1}{6} = \frac{13}{36}$$

4.10.4 NUMERICAL EXAMPLE

Given $C_p = £5$, $C_f = £10$ determine the optimal replacement interval for equipment subject to the replacement strategy of Section 4.10. Failures occur according to the normal distribution with mean = 5 weeks, standard deviation = 1 week.

From equation (4.18) we have

$$C(t_p) = \frac{5 + 10H(t_p)}{t_p}$$

Values of $C(t_p)$ for various values of t_p are given in Table 4.29 from which it is seen that the optimal replacement policy is to perform preventive replacements every four weeks.

Table 4.29

t_p	1	2	3	4	5	6
$C(t_p)$	5·00	2·51	1·74	1·65	2·00	2·24

Sample calculation, for $t_p = 2$ weeks

$$H(2) = [1 + H(1)] \frac{1}{\sqrt{(2\pi)}} \int_{0}^{1} \exp\left[\frac{-(t - 5)^2}{2}\right] dt$$

$$+ [1 + H(0)] \frac{1}{\sqrt{(2\pi)}} \int_{1}^{2} \exp\left[\frac{-(t - 5)^2}{2}\right] dt$$

Now

$$\frac{1}{\sqrt{(2\pi)}} \int_0^1 \exp\left[\frac{-(t-5)^2}{2}\right] dt = \Phi(1-5) = \Phi(-4)$$

(see Figure 4.30)

where $\Phi(t) = \dfrac{1}{\sqrt{(2\pi)}} \displaystyle\int_{-\infty}^t \exp\left[\dfrac{-t^2}{2}\right] dt$ is the cumulative distribution function of the standardized normal distribution whose mean is 0 and standard deviation 1. This function is tabulated in books of statistical tables, as well as in many statistical textbooks.

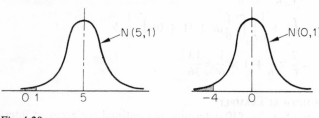

Fig. 4.30

From tables $\Phi(-4) \simeq 0$. Now

$$\frac{1}{\sqrt{(2\pi)}} \int_1^2 \exp\left[\frac{-(t-5)^2}{2}\right] dt = \Phi(-3) - \Phi(-4)$$

$$= 0\cdot0014 - 0 = 0\cdot0014$$

$$H(0) = 0$$

$$H(1) = [1 + H(0)]\frac{1}{\sqrt{(2\pi)}} \int_0^1 \exp\left[\frac{-(t-5)^2}{2}\right] dt$$

$$= (1 + 0)\,0 = 0$$

$$H(2) = (1 + 0)\,0 + (1 + 0)\,0\cdot0014 = 0\cdot0014$$

Therefore

$$C(2) = (5 + 10 \times 0\cdot0014)/2 = £2\cdot50 \text{ per week}$$

4.10.5 FURTHER COMMENTS
In the examples in this section no account was taken of the time required to perform the failure and preventive replacements. When necessary they can be included in the analysis.

4.11 Optimal preventive replacement age of equipment subject to breakdown

4.11.1 STATEMENT OF PROBLEM

This problem is similar to that of Section 4.10 except that instead of making preventive replacements at fixed intervals, thus incurring the possibility of performing a preventive replacement shortly after a failure replacement, the time at which the preventive replacement occurs depends on the age of the equipment. When failures occur failure replacements are made.

Again, the problem is to balance the cost of the preventive replacements against their benefits and we do this by determining the optimal preventive replacement age for the equipment to minimize the total expected cost of replacements per unit time.

4.11.2 CONSTRUCTION OF MODEL

(1) C_p is the cost of a preventive replacement.
(2) C_f is the cost of a failure replacement.
(3) $f(t)$ is the probability density function of the failure times of the equipment.
(4) The replacement policy is to perform a preventive replacement once the equipment has reached a specified age t_p plus failure replacements when necessary. This policy is illustrated in Figure 4.31.

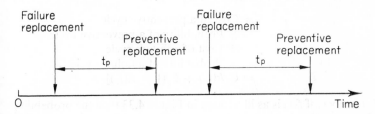

Fig. 4.31

(5) The objective is to determine the optimal replacement age of the equipment to minimize the total expected replacement cost per unit time.

In this problem, there are two possible cycles of operation: one cycle being determined by the equipment reaching its planned replacement age t_p, the other being determined by the equipment ceasing to operate due to a failure occurring before the planned replacement time. These two possible cycles are illustrated in Figure 4.32.

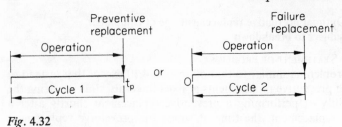

Fig. 4.32

The total expected replacement cost per unit time $C(t_p)$ is

$$C(t_p) = \frac{\text{Total expected replacement cost per cycle}}{\text{Expected cycle length}}$$

Note. We are obtaining the expected cost per unit time as a ratio of two expectations. This is acceptable in many replacement problems since it has been shown that (see Smith [43])

$$\lim_{t \to \infty} \frac{K(t)}{t} = \frac{\text{Expected cost/cycle}}{\text{Expected cycle length}}$$

where $K(t)$ is the cumulative expected cost due to a series of cycles in an interval $(0, t)$. $K(t)/t$ is the expected cost per unit time.

Total expected replacement cost per cycle

$$\begin{aligned}
&= \text{Cost of a preventive cycle} \\
&\quad \times \text{Probability of a preventive cycle} \\
&\quad + \text{Cost of a failure cycle} \\
&\quad \times \text{Probability of a failure cycle} \\
&= C_p R(t_p) + C_f [1 - R(t_p)]
\end{aligned}$$

Remember: if $f(t)$ is as illustrated in Figure 4.33 then the probability of a preventive cycle equals the probability of failure occurring after

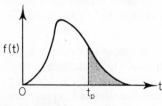

Fig. 4.33

time t_p, that is, it is equivalent to the shaded area, which is denoted $R(t_p)$, (refer to Section 2.5).

The probability of a failure cycle is the probability of a failure occurring before time t_p, which is the unshaded area of Figure 4.33. Since the area under the curve equals unity, then the unshaded area is $[1 - R(t)]$.

> *Expected cycle length* = Length of a preventive cycle
> × Probability of a preventive cycle
> + Expected length of a failure cycle
> × Probability of a failure cycle
> = $t_p \times R(t_p)$ + (expected length of a failure cycle) × $[1 - R(t_p)]$

To determine the expected length of a failure cycle consider Figure 4.34. The mean time to failure of the complete distribution is

$$\int_{-\infty}^{\infty} tf(t)\, dt$$

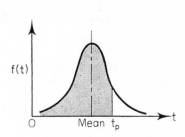

Fig. 4.34

which for the normal distribution equals the mode (peak) of the distribution. If a preventive replacement occurs at time t_p then the mean time to failure is the mean of the shaded portion of Figure 4.34 since the unshaded area is an impossible region for failures. The mean of the shaded area is

$$\int_{-\infty}^{t_p} tf(t)\, dt / [1 - R(t_p)]$$

denoted $M(t_p)$. Therefore

> *Expected cycle length* = $t_p \times R(t_p) + M(t_p) \times [1 - R(t_p)]$

$$C(t_p) = \frac{C_p \times R(t_p) + C_f \times [1 - R(t_p)]}{t_p \times R(t_p) + M(t_p) \times [1 - R(t_p)]} \tag{4.23}$$

This is now a model of the problem relating replacement age t_p to total expected replacement cost per unit time.

4.11.3 NUMERICAL EXAMPLE

For the data of the example in Section 4.10.4 determine the optimal replacement age of the equipment.

Equation (4.23) becomes

$$C(t_p) = \frac{5 \times R(t_p) + 10 \times [1 - R(t_p)]}{t_p \times R(t_p) + \int_{-\infty}^{t_p} tf(t)\, dt}$$

For various values of t_p, the corresponding values of $C(t_p)$ are given in Table 4.30 from which it is seen that the optimal replacement age is four weeks.

Table 4.30

t_p	1	2	3	4	5	6
$C(t_p)$	5·00	2·50	1·70	1·50	1·63	1·87

Sample calculation, for $t_p = 3$ weeks
Equation (4.23) becomes

$$C(3) = \frac{5 \times R(3) + 10 \times [1 - R(3)]}{3 \times R(3) + \int_{-\infty}^{3} tf(t)\, dt}$$

$$R(3) = \frac{1}{\sqrt{(2\pi)}} \int_{3}^{\infty} \exp\left[\frac{-(t-5)^2}{2}\right] dt$$

$$= \frac{1}{\sqrt{(2\pi)}} \int_{-2}^{\infty} \exp\left[\frac{-t^2}{2}\right] dt \quad \text{(see Figure 4.35)}$$

$$= 0·9772$$

Therefore

$$[1 - R(3)] = 1 - 0·9772 = 0·0228$$

$$\int_{-\infty}^{t_p} tf(t)\, dt = \frac{1}{\sigma\sqrt{(2\pi)}} \int_{-\infty}^{t_p} t \exp\left[-\frac{(t-\mu)^2}{2\sigma^2}\right] dt$$

$$= \frac{1}{\sigma\sqrt{(2\pi)}} \int_{-\infty}^{t_p} (t-\mu) \exp\left[-\frac{(t-\mu)^2}{2\sigma^2}\right] dt$$

$$+ \frac{1}{\sigma\sqrt{(2\pi)}} \int_{-\infty}^{t_p} \mu \exp\left[-\frac{(t-\mu)^2}{2\sigma^2}\right] dt$$

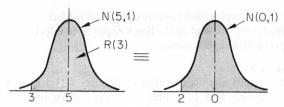

Fig. 4.35

$$= \frac{\sigma}{\sqrt{(2\pi)}} \int_{-\infty}^{t_p} \frac{-d\left(\exp\left[\frac{-(t-\mu)^2}{2\sigma^2}\right]\right)}{dt} + \mu\Phi\left(\frac{t_p-\mu}{\sigma}\right)$$

$$= \frac{-\sigma}{\sqrt{(2\pi)}} \left[\exp\left[\frac{-(t-\mu)^2}{2\sigma^2}\right]\right]_{-\infty}^{t_p} + \mu\Phi\left(\frac{t_p-\mu}{\sigma}\right)$$

$$= \frac{-\sigma}{\sqrt{(2\pi)}} \exp\left[\frac{-(t_p-\mu)^2}{2\sigma^2}\right] + \mu\Phi\left(\frac{t_p-\mu}{\sigma}\right)$$

$$= -\sigma\,\phi\left(\frac{t_p-\mu}{\sigma}\right) + \mu\Phi\left(\frac{t_p-\mu}{\sigma}\right)$$

where $\phi(t) = \dfrac{1}{\sqrt{(2\pi)}} \exp\left[\dfrac{-t^2}{2}\right]$ and $\Phi(t) = \dfrac{1}{\sqrt{(2\pi)}} \int_{-\infty}^{t} \exp\left[\dfrac{-t^2}{2}\right] dt$

$\phi(t)$ and $\Phi(t)$ are the ordinate and cumulative distribution functions at t of the standardized normal distribution whose mean is 0, standard deviation 1.

When $\sigma = 1$, $\mu = 5$ then

$$\int_{-\infty}^{3} tf(t)\,dt = -\phi\left(\frac{3-5}{1}\right) + 5\Phi\left(\frac{3-5}{1}\right)$$

$$= -0.0540 + 5 \times 0.0228 = 0.0600$$

where 0·0540 and 0·0228 are obtained from tables of the standardized normal distribution.

Therefore

$$C(3) = \frac{5 \times 0.9772 + 10 \times 0.0228}{3 \times 0.9772 + 0.0600} = £1.70 \text{ per week}$$

4.11.4 FURTHER COMMENTS

As was the case for the example in Section 4.10 no account has been taken of the time required to effect a failure or preventive replacement. When necessary the replacement times can be catered for in the model and in the following Section 4.12 the model will include the times required to effect either a failure or preventive replacement.

4.12 Optimal preventive replacement age of equipment subject to breakdown, taking account of the times required to effect failure and preventive replacements

4.12.1 STATEMENT OF PROBLEM

The problem definition is identical to that of Section 4.11.1 except that, instead of assuming that the failure and preventive replacements are made instantaneously, account is taken of the time required to make these replacements.

The optimal preventive replacement age of the equipment is again taken as that age which minimizes the total expected cost of replacements per unit time.

4.12.2 CONSTRUCTION OF MODEL

(1) C_p is the cost of a preventive replacement.

(2) C_f is the cost of a failure replacement.

(3) T_p is the time required to make a preventive replacement.

(4) T_f is the time required to make a failure replacement.

(5) $f(t)$ is the probability density function of the failure times of the equipment.

(6) $M(t_p)$ is the mean time to failure when preventive replacement occurs at time t_p.

(7) The replacement policy is to perform a preventive replacement once the equipment has reached a specified age t_p, plus failure replacements when necessary. This policy is illustrated in Figure 4.36.

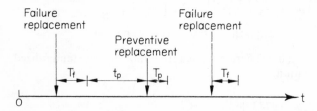

Fig. 4.36

(8) The objective is to determine the optimal preventive replacement age of the equipment to minimize the total expected replacement cost per unit time.

As was the case for the problem of Section 4.11 there are two possible cycles of operation and they are illustrated in Figure 4.37.

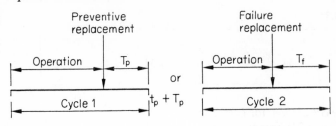

Fig. 4.37

The total expected replacement cost per unit time, denoted $C(t_p)$, is

$$C(t_p) = \frac{\text{Total expected replacement cost per cycle}}{\text{Expected cycle length}}$$

Total expected replacement $= C_p \times R(t_p) + C_f[1 - R(t_p)]$
cost per cycle
(as per Section 4.11.2)

Expected cycle length = Length of a preventive cycle
$\times$ Probability of a preventive cycle
$+$ Expected length of a failure cycle
$\times$ Probability of a failure cycle
$= (t_p + T_p)R(t_p)$
$+ [M(t_p) + T_f][1 - R(t_p)]$

$$C(t_p) = \frac{C_p R(t_p) + C_f[1 - R(t_p)]}{(t_p + T_p)R(t_p) + [M(t_p) + T_f][1 - R(t_p)]} \qquad (4.24)$$

This is a model of the problem relating preventive replacement age t_p to the total expected replacement cost per unit time.

4.12.3 NUMERICAL EXAMPLE

For the data of Section 4.10.4 namely $C_p = £5$, $C_f = £10$, $f(t) = N(5, 1)$, and replacement times T_p and $T_f = \frac{1}{2}$ week determine the optimal replacement age of the equipment.

Equation (4.24) becomes

$$C(t_p) = \frac{5 \times R(t_p) + 10[1 - R(t_p)]}{(t_p + 0.5)R(t_p) + \int_{-\infty}^{t_p} tf(t)\, dt + 0.5[1 - R(t_p)]}$$

For various values of t_p, the corresponding values of $C(t_p)$ are given in Table 4.31 from which it is seen that the optimal preventive replacement age is four weeks.

Table 4.31

t_p	1	2	3	4	5	6
$C(t_p)$	3·34	2·00	1·46	1·34	1·47	1·70

Sample calculation, for $t_p = 3$ weeks
Equation (4.24) becomes:

$$C(3) = \frac{5 \times R(3) + 10 \times [1 - R(3)]}{3\cdot5 \times R(3) + 0\cdot0600 + 0\cdot5[1 - R(3)]}$$

$$= \frac{5 \times 0\cdot9772 + 10 \times 0\cdot0228}{3\cdot5 \times 0\cdot9772 + 0\cdot0600 + 0\cdot0114}$$

$$= 5\cdot1140/3\cdot4974 = £1\cdot46 \text{ per week}$$

4.13 Optimal preventive replacement interval or age of equipment subject to breakdown: minimization of downtime

4.13.1 STATEMENT OF PROBLEM

The problems of Section 4.10–4.12 had as their objective to "minimize total cost per unit time". In some cases, say due to difficulties in costing or the desire to get maximum throughput or utilization of equipment, the replacement policy required may be one which minimizes total downtime per unit time. The problem of this section is to determine the best times at which replacements should occur to minimize total downtime per unit time. The basic conflicts are that as the preventive replacement frequency increases there is an increase in downtime due to these replacements, but a consequence of this is a reduction of downtime due to failure replacements, and we wish to get the best balance between them.

4.13.2 CONSTRUCTION OF MODELS

(1) T_f is the downtime required to make a failure replacement.
(2) T_p is the downtime required to make a preventive replacement.
(3) $f(t)$ is the probability density function of the failure times of the equipment.

Model 1—Determination of optimal preventive replacement interval

(4) The objective is to determine the optimal replacement interval t_p between preventive replacements to minimize total downtime per unit time. The policy is illustrated in Figure 4.38.

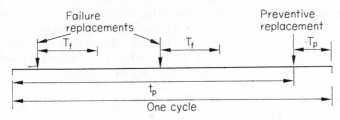

Fig. 4.38

The total downtime per unit time, for preventive replacement at time t_p, denoted $D(t_p)$ is

$$D(t_p) = \frac{\begin{array}{l} \text{Expected downtime due to failures} \\ + \text{ Downtime due to preventive replacement} \end{array}}{\text{Cycle length}}$$

Downtime due to failures = Number of failures in interval $(0, t_p)$
$\qquad\qquad\qquad\qquad\qquad\times$ Time required to make a failure replacement

$$= H(t_p) \times T_f$$

Downtime due to preventive replacement $= T_p$
Therefore

$$D(t_p) = \frac{H(t_p)T_f + T_p}{t_p + T_p} \tag{4.25}$$

This is a model of the problem relating replacement interval t_p to total downtime $D(t_p)$.

Model 2—Determination of optimal preventive replacement age

(5) The objective is to determine the optimal age t_p at which preventive replacements should occur such that total downtime per unit time is minimized. The policy was illustrated earlier in Figure 4.37 from which it is seen that there are two possible cycles of operation.

The total downtime per unit time for preventive replacements once the equipment becomes of age t_p is

$$D(t_p) = \frac{\text{Total expected downtime/cycle}}{\text{Expected cycle length}}$$

Total expected downtime/cycle = Downtime due to a preventive cycle
$\times$ Probability of a preventive cycle
+ Downtime due to a failure cycle
$\times$ Probability of a failure cycle
$= T_p R(t_p) + T_f[1 - R(t_p)]$

Expected cycle length $= (t_p + T_p)R(t_p) + [M(t_p) + T_f][1 - R(t_p)]$
(as per Section 4.12.2)

Therefore

$$D(t_p) = \frac{T_p R(t_p) + T_f[1 - R(t_p)]}{(t_p + T_p)R(t_p) + [M(t_p) + T_f][1 - R(t_p)]} \qquad (4.26)$$

This is a model of the problem relating replacement age to total downtime.

4.13.3 NUMERICAL EXAMPLES
Let $T_f = 0.07$ week, $T_p = 0.035$ week, $f(t) = N(5, 1)$.

Model 1—Replacement interval
From equation (4.25) we have

$$D(t_p) = \frac{H(t_p)0.07 + 0.035}{t_p + 0.035}$$

Table 4.32 gives values of $D(t_p)$ for various values of t_p and it is seen that the optimal replacement interval is $t_p = 4$ weeks

Table 4.32

t_p	1	2	3	4	5	6
$D(t_p)$	0·0338	0·0173	0·0121	0·0114	0·0139	0·0156

Model 2—Replacement age
From equation (4.26) we have

$$D(t_p) = \frac{0.035R(t_p) + 0.07[1 - R(t_p)]}{(t_p + 0.035)R(t_p) + [M(t_p) + 0.07][1 - R(t_p)]} \qquad (4.27)$$

Since

$$M(t_p) = \frac{\displaystyle\int_{-\infty}^{t_p} tf(t)\,dt}{1 - R(t_p)}$$

then equation (4.27) becomes

$$D(t_p) = \frac{0 \cdot 035 R(t_p) + 0 \cdot 07[1 - R(t_p)]}{(t_p + 0 \cdot 035)R(t_p) + \int_{-\infty}^{t_p} tf(t)\, dt + 0 \cdot 07[1 - R(t_p)]} \qquad (4.28)$$

Inserting different values of t_p into equation (4.28) Table 4.33 can be constructed from which it is seen that the optimal replacement age is 4 weeks.

Table 4.33

t_p	1	2	3	4	5	6
$D(t_p)$	0·0338	0·0221	0·0118	0·0102	0·0113	0·0129

Sample calculations
Model 1—Replacement interval
When $t_p = 3$, then equation (4.25) becomes

$$D(2) = \frac{H(2) \times 0 \cdot 07 + 0 \cdot 035}{3 + 0 \cdot 035}$$

$$H(2) = 0 \cdot 0014 \qquad \text{(from Section 4.10.4)}$$

Therefore

$$D(2) = 0 \cdot 0173$$

Model 2—Replacement age
When $t_p = 3$, then equation (4.26) becomes

$$D(3) = \frac{0 \cdot 035 R(3) + 0 \cdot 07[1 - R(3)]}{(3 + 0 \cdot 035)R(3) + \int_{-\infty}^{3} tf(t)\, dt + 0 \cdot 07[1 - R(3)]}$$

From Section 4.11.3,

$$R(3) = 0 \cdot 9772 \qquad 1 - R(3) = 0 \cdot 0228 \qquad \int_{-\infty}^{3} tf(t)\, dt = 0 \cdot 0600$$

Therefore

$$D(3) = 0 \cdot 0118$$

4.13.4 FURTHER COMMENTS
With reference to Model 1, provided that the time required to effect a failure replacement is small relative to the intervals being considered

for preventive replacement (e.g. 0·07 as against 4), it is reasonable to use the $H(T)$ formulation of Section 4.10.3 to determine the expected number of failures in interval $(0, t_p)$. Strictly, account should be taken of the fact that the time available between preventive replacements for failure to occur is reduced due to any downtime which is incurred to make failure replacements.

Note also that although the replacement interval and replacement age to minimize downtime are both 4 weeks the age-based policy reduces downtime, for the figures used in the example, by 10·5% when compared with the interval based policy.

4.14 Group replacement: optimal interval between group replacement of items which are subject to failure: the lamp replacement problem

It is sometimes worthwhile to replace similar items in groups, rather than singly, since the cost of replacing an item under group replacement conditions may be lower, i.e. there are economies of scale. Perhaps the classic example of this sort of situation is that of maintenance of street lamps. Bearing in mind the cost of transporting a lighting department's maintenance staff to a single street lamp failure and discounts associated with bulk purchase of lamps, it may pay them to replace all the lamps in the street rather than only the failure.

This particular type of problem is virtually identical to that of Section 4.10, except that here we are dealing with a group of identical items, rather than single items.

4.14.1 STATEMENT OF PROBLEM

There are a large number of similar items which are subject to failure Whenever an item fails it is replaced by a new item. (We do not assume group replacement (i.e. replacing all items at the same time) in such conditions.) There is also the possibility that group replacement can be performed at fixed intervals of time. The cost of replacing an item under group replacement conditions is assumed to be less than that for failure replacement. The more frequently group replacement is performed the less failure replacements will occur, but a balance is required between the money spent on group replacement and the reduction of failure replacements.

The model developed for this problem is based on the assumption that the replacement policy is to perform group replacements at fixed intervals of time, with failure replacements occurring as necessary, and we wish to determine the optimal interval between the group replacements to minimize the total expected cost of replacement per unit time.

4.14.2 CONSTRUCTION OF MODEL

(1) C_g is the cost of replacing one item under conditions of group replacement.
(2) C_f is the cost of a failure replacement.
(3) $f(t)$ is the probability density function of the failure times of the items.
(4) N is the total number of items in the group.
(5) The replacement policy is to perform group replacement at constant intervals of length t_p, with failure replacements occurring as many times as required in interval $(0, t_p)$. The policy is illustrated in Figure 4.39.

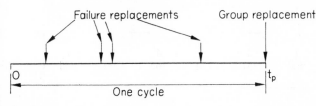

Fig. 4.39

(6) The objective is to determine the optimal interval between group replacements to minimize the total expected replacement cost per unit time.

The total expected replacement cost per unit time, for group replacement at time t_p, denoted $C(t_p)$ is

$$C(t_p) = \frac{\text{Total expected cost in interval } (0, t_p)}{\text{Interval length}}$$

Total expected cost in interval $(0, t_p)$ = Cost of group replacement at time t_p + Expected cost of failure replacements in interval $(0, t_p)$

$$= NC_g + NH(t_p)C_f$$

where $H(t_p)$ is the expected number of times one item fails in interval $(0, t_p)$. The method of determining $H(t_p)$ is given in Section 4.10.3. Therefore

$$C(t_p) = \frac{NC_g + NH(t_p)C_f}{t_p} \tag{4.29}$$

This is a model of the group replacement problem relating replacement interval t_p to total cost.

4.14.3 NUMERICAL EXAMPLE
Using the data given in the example of Section 4.10.4, namely:

   (i) cost of a failure replacement = £10
  (ii) cost of a replacement under group replacement conditions
       = £5
 (iii) $f(t) = N(5, 1)$

and assuming that there are 100 items in the group Table 4.34 can
be constructed. It gives values of $C(t_p)$, the total replacement cost per
unit time, for various values of t_p, the group replacement interval,
from which it is seen that the optimal interval between group replacements is 4 weeks.

Table 4.34

t_p	1	2	3	4	5	6
$C(t_p)$	500	251	174	165	200	224

Sample calculation for $t_p = 2$ weeks
Equation (4.29) becomes

$$C(2) = [100 \times 5 + 100H(2)10]/2$$
$$H(2) = 0{\cdot}0014 \quad \text{(from example in Section 4.10.4)}$$

Therefore

$$C(2) = (500 + 1{\cdot}4)/2 = £251$$

4.14.4 FURTHER COMMENTS
Note that the optimal group replacement interval for the above
example is identical to the optimal preventive replacement interval
for a single item as given in Section 4.10. The minimum total replacement cost for group replacement is the same as that for a single unit,
multiplied by the number of items in the group.

4.15 Further replacement models
Two further replacement models not covered previously in the
text are outlined for the interested reader. In both cases the level of
mathematics used is of a slightly higher order than that of this book.

4.15.1 MULTI-STAGE REPLACEMENT
A multi-stage replacement strategy may be relevant to the situation
where there is a group of similar items which can be divided into sub-
groups dependent upon the cost of replacing an item on its failure.

For example some items may be more expensive to replace than others due to failure in a key position having expensive repercussions.

A two-stage replacement strategy is examined in a paper by Bartholomew [2]. The problem examined is one where there are N similar items divided into two groups, N_1 and N_2, and the costs of replacement of an item in these groups are C_1 and C_2 respectively. The two-stage replacement strategy is illustrated in Figure 4.40.

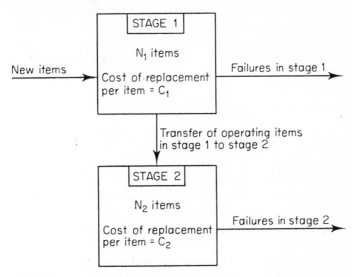

Fig. 4.40

For Figure 4.40 it is assumed that the cost of replacement in stage 1 is greater than that of stage 2. In this case all failures which occur in stage 2 are replaced by operating items from stage 1. Vacancies which occur in stage 1, whether caused by failure or transfer of operating items to stage 2, are replaced by new items. Although this strategy does not reduce the overall steady state failure rate of the system it does decrease it in stage 1 (where replacement cost is high) and increase it in stage 2 (where replacement cost is low). In Bartholomew's paper the conditions are derived for two-stage replacement to be preferable to simple replacement (i.e. replacing any failure directly with a new item).

A possible application of such a strategy relates to replacement of tyres on vehicles. For example, if a failure occurs in a rear tyre, and it is to be replaced, then it is replaced by a tyre from one of the front wheels and the new tyre is placed on the front wheel.

The two-stage strategy is extended in a paper by Naik and Nair [35] to cater for the possibility of defining several stages in a system, each stage being defined by its replacement cost.

4.15.2 OPTIONAL POLICIES

Frequently equipment ceases to operate, not because of its own failure but because there is a production stoppage for some reason. When this occurrence arises the maintenance manager may be faced with having to decide whether or not to take advantage of the down-time opportunity to perform a preventive replacement.

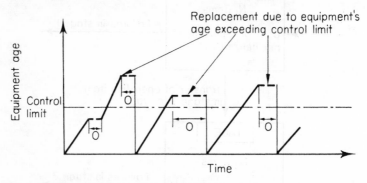

Fig. 4.41. O = replacement opportunities.

Woodman [52] discussed this problem and constructs a model to cover optional policies (so called because the decision on whether or not to take advantage of the downtime opportunity is at the option of the manager). Basically the model takes account of the costs of failure replacement, cost of replacement during downtime, the failure distribution of the equipment subject to replacement, and the frequency with which "replacement opportunities" occur. Solution of the model results in control limits being determined which enable the manager to determine whether or not to take advantage of the opportunity, depending on the age of the equipment. This policy is illustrated in Figure 4.41. If an equipment failure occurs it is replaced. If a replacement opportunity occurs and the equipment's age exceeds the control limit a preventive replacement is made, otherwise the equipment is left during the "opportunity" and allowed to continue operating.

5 Inspection Decisions

5.1 Introduction

The problems of this chapter are concerned with determining inspection schedules, i.e. the points in time at which the inspection action should take place.

The basic purpose behind an inspection is to determine the state of equipment. Once indicators, such as bearing wear, gauge readings, quality of product, which are used to describe the state have been specified, and the inspection made to determine the values of these indicators, then some further maintenance action may be taken, depending on the state. When the inspection should take place ought to be influenced by the costs of the inspection (which will be related to the indicator(s) used to describe the state of the equipment) and the benefits of the inspection, such as detection and correction of minor defects before major breakdown occurs.

5.2 Optimal inspection frequency: maximization of profit

5.2.1 STATEMENT OF PROBLEM

Equipment breaks down from time to time, requiring materials and tradesmen to repair it. Also, while the equipment is being repaired there is a loss in production output. In order to reduce the number of breakdowns, we can periodically inspect the equipment and rectify any minor defects which may eventually cause complete breakdown. These inspections cost money in terms of materials, wages and loss of production due to scheduled downtime.

What we want to determine is an inspection policy which will give us the correct balance between the number of inspections and the resulting output such that the profit per unit time from the equipment is maximized over a long period.

5.2.2 CONSTRUCTION OF MODEL

(1) Equipment failures occur according to the negative exponential distribution with mean time to failure (MTTF) = $1/\lambda$, where λ is the mean arrival rate of failures. (For example, if the MTTF

= 0·5 years, then the mean number of failures per year = 1/0·5
= 2, i.e. $\lambda = 2$.)

(2) Repair times are negative exponentially distributed with mean time $1/\mu$.

(3) The inspection policy is to perform n inspections per unit time. Inspection times are negative exponentially distributed with mean time $1/i$.

(4) The value of the output in an uninterrupted unit of time has a profit value V (e.g. selling price less material cost less production cost). That is, V is the profit value if there are no downtime losses.

(5) The average cost of inspection per uninterrupted unit of time is I.

(6) The average cost of repairs per uninterrupted unit of time is R.

Note that I and R are the costs which would be incurred if inspection or repair lasted the whole unit of time. The actual costs incurred per unit time will be proportions of I and R.

(7) The breakdown rate of the equipment, λ, is a function of n, the frequency of inspection. That is, the breakdowns can be influenced by the number of inspections, therefore, $\lambda \equiv \lambda(n)$, as illustrated in Figure 5.1.

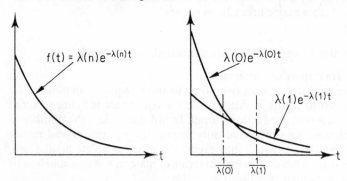

Fig. 5.1

In Figure 5.1

$\lambda(0)$ = breakdown rate if no inspections are made
$\lambda(1)$ = breakdown rate if 1 inspection is made

Thus from the Figure it can be seen that the effect of performing inspections is to increase the mean time to failure of the equipment.

(8) The objective is to choose *n* in order to maximize the expected profit per unit time from operating the equipment. The basic conflicts are illustrated in Figure 5.2.

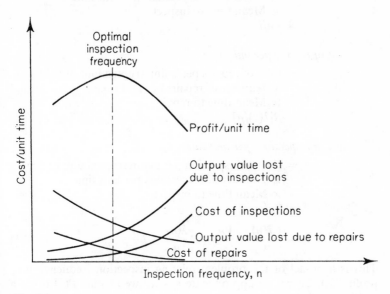

Fig. 5.2.

The profit per unit time from operating the equipment will be a function of the number of inspections. Therefore denoting profit per unit time by $P(n)$,

$P(n) =$ Value of output per uninterrupted unit of time
         — Ouput value lost due to repairs per unit time
         — Output value lost due to inspections per unit time
         — Cost of repairs per unit time
         — Cost of inspections per unit time.

Output value lost due to repairs per unit time

       $=$ Value of output per uninterrupted unit of time
         $\times$ Number of repairs per unit time
         $\times$ Mean time to repair
       $= V\lambda(n)/\mu$

Note that $\lambda(n)/\mu$ is the proportion of unit time which a job spends being repaired.

Output value lost due to inspections per unit time

> = Value of output per uninterrupted unit of time
> × Number of inspections per unit time
> × Mean time to inspect
> = Vn/i

Cost of repairs per unit time

> = Cost of repairs per uninterrupted unit of time
> × Number of repairs per unit time
> × Mean time to repair
> = $R[\lambda(n)/\mu]$

Cost of inspections per unit time

> = Cost of inspection per uninterrupted unit of time
> × Number of inspections per unit time
> × Mean time to inspect
> = $I(n/i)$

$$P(n) = V - \frac{V\lambda(n)}{\mu} - \frac{Vn}{i} - R\frac{\lambda(n)}{\mu} - I\frac{n}{i} \qquad (5.1)$$

This is a model of the problem relating inspection frequency n to profit $P(n)$. To get an approximate answer we assume $P(n)$ to be a continuous function of n, so

$$\frac{dP(n)}{dn} = -\frac{V\lambda'(n)}{\mu} - \frac{V}{i} - R\frac{\lambda'(n)}{\mu} - \frac{I}{i}$$

where $\lambda'(n) = d[\lambda(n)]/dn$.

Therefore

$$0 = \frac{\lambda'(n)}{\mu}(V + R) + \frac{1}{i}(V + I)$$

$$\text{Maximum } \lambda'(n) = -\frac{\mu}{i}\left(\frac{V + I}{V + R}\right) \qquad (5.2)$$

Since values of μ, i, V, R, I and the form of $\lambda(n)$ are known the optimal frequency to maximize profit per unit time is that value of n which makes the left-hand side of equation (5.2) equal to its right-hand side.

5.2.3 NUMERICAL EXAMPLE

Assume that the breakdown rate varies inversely with the number of inspections, that is, $\lambda(n) = k/n$ which gives

$$\lambda'(n) = -k/n^2 \qquad (5.3)$$

Note that the constant k can be interpreted as the arrival rate of breakdowns per unit time when one inspection is made per unit time.

Substituting equation (5.3) into equation (5.2) the optimal value of n is that value for which

$$n = \sqrt{\left[\frac{ik}{\mu} \left(\frac{V + R}{V + I} \right) \right]}$$

Let

Average number of breakdowns per month, k
$\qquad\qquad = 3$ (i.e., when 1 inspection is made)
Mean time to perform a repair $1/\mu = 24$ hours $= 0 \cdot 033$ month
Mean time to perform an inspection $1/i = 8$ hours
$\qquad\qquad\qquad = 0 \cdot 011$ month
Value of output per uninterrupted month $V = £30\,000$
Cost of repair per uninterrupted month $R = £250$
Cost of inspection per uninterrupted month $I = £125$

$$n = \sqrt{\left[\frac{3 \times 0 \cdot 033}{0 \cdot 011} \left(\frac{30\,000 + 250}{30\,000 + 125} \right) \right]} = 3 \cdot 006$$

Thus, the optimal number of inspections per month in order to maximize profit is 3.

Substitution of $n = 3$ into equation (5.1) will of course give the expected profit per unit time resulting from this policy. Insertion of other values of n into equation (5.1) will give the expected profit resulting from other inspection policies and comparisons can be made with the savings of the optimal policy over other possibilities, and over the policy currently adopted for the equipment.

5.2.4 FURTHER COMMENTS

The most important point to note from this problem is that it is concerned with identifying the best level of preventive maintenance (in the form of inspections and consequent minor overhauls and replacements) when the failure rate of equipment is constant. For many complex equipments the failure distribution is negative exponential, although some individual components of the equipment may exhibit wearout characteristics. The effect of the inspections is that certain potential component failures will be identified which, if left alone, would cause failure of the complete equipment. Components will, of course, still cause equipment failure and the overall failure distribution of the equipment will in most cases remain negative exponential, but with a reduced rate of failure. Figure 5.3 illustrates that the effect of performing inspections is to reduce the

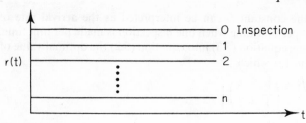

Fig. 5.3

level of the failure rate and, in effect, the problem is to identify the best failure rate.

The assumption was implied in the inspection problem that the depth (or level) of inspection was specified (e.g. open up equipment and take measurements x, y, z; compare with standards; renew or do not renew components). There may also be the problem of identifying the best level of inspection. The greater the depth the greater the inspection cost, but there is perhaps a greater chance that potential failures will be detected. In this case a balance would be required between the costs of the various possible levels of inspection and the resulting benefits, such as reduced downtime due to failures.

Before leaving this problem it is worth noting that, in practice, relating the failure rate of the equipment to the frequency of inspection may be a difficult problem. One method of attack is experimentation with one's own equipment. Alternatively, if several companies have the same type of equipment, doing much the same type of work, collaboration amongst the companies may result in determining how the failure rate is influenced by various inspection policies.

5.3 Optimal inspection frequency: minimization of downtime

5.3.1 STATEMENT OF PROBLEM
The problem of this section is analogous to that of Section 5.2.1, namely, equipment breaks down from time to time and, to reduce the breakdowns, inspections and consequent minor modifications can be made. The problem is to determine the inspection policy which minimizes the total downtime per unit time incurred due to breakdowns and inspections, rather than to determine the policy which maximizes profit per unit time.

5.3.2 CONSTRUCTION OF MODEL
(1) $f(t)$, $\lambda(n)$, n, $1/\mu$ and $1/i$ are defined in Section 5.2.2.
(2) The objective is to choose n to minimize total downtime per unit time.

The total downtime per unit time will be a function of the inspection frequency, n, denoted $D(n)$. Therefore

$D(n) =$ Downtime incurred due to repairs per unit time
$\qquad +$ Downtime incurred due to inspection per unit time

$$= \frac{\lambda(n)}{\mu} + \frac{n}{i} \qquad (5.4)$$

Equation (5.4) is a model of the problem relating inspection frequency n to total downtime $D(n)$.

5.3.3 NUMERICAL EXAMPLE

Using the data of the example of Section 5.2.3 and assuming $D(n)$ to be a continuous function of n,

$$D(n) = \frac{\lambda(n)}{\mu} + \frac{n}{i} \qquad \text{(from equation 5.4)}$$

Now $\lambda'(n) = -k/n^2$ and therefore

$$D'(n) = -\frac{k}{n^2\mu} + \frac{1}{i} = 0$$

Therefore

$$n = \sqrt{\frac{ki}{\mu}} = \sqrt{\frac{3 \times 0.033}{0.011}} = 3 \text{ inspections/month}$$

5.3.4 FURTHER COMMENTS

It will be noted that the optimal inspection frequency to minimize downtime for the above example is the same as when it is required to maximize profit (Section 5.2.3). This is not always the case. The models used to determine the frequencies are different (equations 5.1 and 5.4) and it is only because of the specific cost figures used in the previous example that the solutions are identical for both examples.

Note also that if the problem of this section had been to determine the optimal inspection frequency to maximize availability then this would be equivalent to minimizing downtime (since availability/unit time $= 1 -$ downtime/unit time). Thus, in the above example where the optimal value of $n = 3$, the minimum total downtime per month is (from equation 5.4)

$$D(3) = \frac{3 \times 0.033}{3} + 3 \times 0.011 = 0.066 \text{ month}$$

Maximum availability $= (1 - 0.066)$ month $\equiv 93.4\%$

5.4 Optimal inspection interval to maximize the availability of equipment used in emergency conditions

5.4.1 STATEMENT OF PROBLEM

Equipment such as fire extinguishers and many military weapons are stored for use in an emergency. If the equipment can deteriorate while in storage there is the risk that when it is called into use it will not function. To reduce the probability that equipment will be inoperable when required, inspections can be made, and if equipment is found to be in a failed state, it can be repaired or replaced, thus returning it to the as new condition. Inspection and repair or replacement takes time and the problem is to determine the best interval between inspections to maximize the proportion of time that the equipment is in the available state.

5.4.2 CONSTRUCTION OF MODEL

(1) $f(t)$ is the density function of the time to failure of the equipment.

(2) T_i is the time required to effect an inspection. It is assumed that after the inspection, if no major faults are found requiring repair or complete equipment replacement, then the equipment is in the as new state. This may be as a result of minor modifications being made during the inspection.

(3) T_r is the time required to effect a repair or replacement. After the repair or replacement it is assumed that the equipment is in the as new state.

(4) The objective is to determine the interval t_i between inspections to maximize availability per unit time.

Figure 5.4 illustrates the two possible cycles of operation.

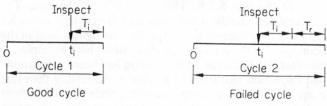

Fig. 5.4

The availability per unit time will be a function of the inspection interval t_i and denoting this by $A(t_i)$,

$$A(t_i) = \frac{\text{Expected availability per cycle}}{\text{Expected cycle length}}$$

The availability in a good cycle equals t_i if no failure is detected at the inspection. If a failure is detected then the availability of the failed cycle can be taken as the mean time to failure of the equipment, given that inspection takes place at t_i.

Thus the *expected availability per cycle* is

$$t_iR(t_i) + \frac{\displaystyle\int_{-\infty}^{t_i} tf(t)\,dt}{1 - R(t_i)}\,[1 - R(t_i)] \qquad \text{(cf denominator of equation 4.23)}$$

$$= t_iR(t_i) + \int_{-\infty}^{t_i} tf(t)\,dt$$

The *expected cycle length* is:

$$(t_i + T_i)R(t_i) + (t_i + T_i + T_r)[1 - R(t_i)]$$

Therefore

$$A(t_i) = \frac{t_iR(t_i) + \displaystyle\int_{-\infty}^{t_i} tf(t)\,dt}{t_i + T_i + T_r[1 - R(t_i)]} \qquad (5.5)$$

This is a model of the problem relating inspection interval t_i to availability per unit time $A(t_i)$.

5.4.3 NUMERICAL EXAMPLE

(1) The time to failure of equipment is normally distributed with mean of 5 months and standard deviation 1 month.
(2) $T_i = 0.25$ month.
(3) $T_r = 0.50$ month.

Equation (5.5) becomes

$$A(t_i) = \frac{t_iR(t_i) + \displaystyle\int_{-\infty}^{t_i} tf(t)\,dt}{t_i + 0.25 + 0.50\,[1 - R(t_i)]}$$

Table 5.1 results from evaluating the right-hand side of equation (5.5) for various values of t_i. The optimal inspection interval to maximize availability is seen to be 3 months.

Table 5.1

t_i	1	2	3	4	5	6
$A(t_i)$	0.8000	0.8905	0.9173	0.9047	0.8366	0.7371

Sample calculation
When $t_i = 3$ months,

$$\int_{-\infty}^{3} tf(t)\, dt = 0 \cdot 0600 \qquad R(3) = 0 \cdot 9772 \qquad 1 - R(3) = 0 \cdot 0228$$

(see Section 4.11.3)

Therefore equation (5.5) becomes

$$A(3) = \frac{3 \times 0 \cdot 9772 + 0 \cdot 0600}{3 + 0 \cdot 25 + 0 \cdot 5(0 \cdot 0225)} = 0 \cdot 9173$$

5.4.4 FURTHER COMMENTS
The crucial assumption in the model of this section is that equipment can be assumed to be as good as new after inspection if no repair or replacement takes place. In practice this may be reasonable and it will certainly be the case if the failure distribution of the equipment was negative exponential (since the conditional probability remains constant).

If the as new assumption is not realistic and the failure distribution has an increasing failure rate then rather than having inspection at constant intervals it may be worthwhile increasing the inspection frequency the older the equipment gets. Such a problem is covered in the following section.

5.5 Optimal inspection schedule for equipment whose condition can only be determined through inspection: minimization of total cost

5.5.1 STATEMENT OF PROBLEM
Equipment used as part of a production process is subject to failure which might be of the form of producing goods outside tolerance limits. The state of the equipment, good or failed, can only be determined by an inspection, for example, by checking the quality of the machine output. When failure is detected then the equipment is returned to the as new condition as a result of a repair and the production cycle is begun again. The problem is to determine an optimal inspection schedule to minimize the total costs per unit time associated with inspection, repair and non-detection of failed equipment.

5.5.2 CONSTRUCTION OF MODEL
(1) $f(t)$ is the density function of the time to failure of the equipment.
(2) C_i is the cost of an inspection.

(3) C_u is the cost per unit time associated with an undetected failed equipment (e.g. it may be scrap cost, re-working cost, lost production cost).
(4) C_r is the cost of a repair.
(5) T_r is the time required to effect a repair.
(6) The inspection policy is to perform inspections at times x_1, x_2, x_3 . . ., until a failed equipment is detected. The policy is illustrated in Figure 5.5 for one possible cycle of operation.

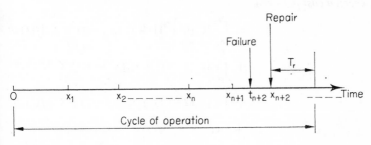

Fig. 5.5

Note that the intervals between the inspections are not necessarily constant but may reduce if the chance of failure increases.
(7) The objective is to determine the optimal inspection schedule to minimize total costs per unit time.

The expected total cost per unit time of inspection and repairing the equipment will be a function of the schedule of inspection times x_1, x_2, x_3 . . .. Denoting this by $C(x_1, x_2, x_3 . . .)$ we get:

$$C(x_1, x_2, x_3 . . .) = \frac{\text{Total expected costs per cycle } E_c(x_1, x_2, x_3 . . .)}{\text{Expected cycle length } E_l(x_1, x_2, x_3 . . .)}$$

Now, failure of the equipment can occur between any pair of inspection times. Thus, if failure occurred between time 0 and x_1, say at t_1, the cost of the cycle would be

$$C_i(1) + C_u(x_1 - t_1) + C_r$$

and the expected value of this is

$$\int_0^{x_1} [C_i(1) + C_u(x_1 - t) + C_r] f(t) \, dt$$

If failure occurred between x_1 and x_2, say at time t_2, the cost of the cycle would be

$$C_i(1 + 1) + C_u(x_2 - t_2) + C_r$$

and the expected value of this would be

$$\int_{x_1}^{x_2} [C_i(1 + 1) + C_u(x_2 - t) + C_r]f(t)\, dt$$

In a manner similar to the above, the costs and probabilities of all possible cycles can be determined to give the expected cost per cycle as:

Expected cost per cycle

$$= \int_0^{x_1} [C_i(0 + 1) + C_u(x_1 - t) + C_r]f(t)\, dt$$

$$+ \int_{x_1}^{x_2} [C_i(1 + 1) + C_u(x_2 - t) + C_r]f(t)\, dt$$

$$+ \int_{x_2}^{x_3} [C_i(2 + 1) + C_u(x_3 - t) + C_r]f(t)\, dt$$

$$+ \text{etc.}$$

Therefore

$$E_c(x_1, x_2, x_3 \ldots)$$

$$= \sum_{k=0}^{\infty} \int_{x_k}^{x_{k+1}} [(C_i(k + 1) + C_u(x_{k+1} - t) + C_r]f(t)\, dt$$

$$= C_r + \sum_{k=0}^{\infty} \int_{x_k}^{x_{k+1}} [C_i(k + 1) + C_u(x_{k+1} - t)]f(t)\, dt$$

In a manner similar to that adopted to determine the expected costs per cycle the *expected cycle length* can be determined as

$$\int_0^{x_1} [t + (x_1 - t) + T_r]f(t)\, dt$$

$$+ \int_{x_1}^{x_2} [t + (x_2 - t) + T_r]f(t)\, dt$$

$$+ \int_{x_2}^{x_3} [t + (x_3 - t) + T_r]f(t)\, dt + \text{etc.}$$

Therefore

$$E_l(x_1, x_2, x_3 \ldots) = \mu + T_r + \sum_{k=0}^{\infty} \int_{x_k}^{x_{k+1}} (x_{k+1} - t)f(t)\, dt$$

where μ is the mean time to failure of the equipment.

Thus

$$C(x_1, x_2, x_3 \ldots) = \frac{C_r + \sum_{k=0}^{\infty} \int_{x_k}^{x_{k+1}} [C_i(k+1) + C_u(x_{k+1}-t)]f(t)\,dt}{\mu + T_r + \sum_{k=0}^{\infty} \int_{x_k}^{x_{k+1}} (x_{k+1}-t)f(t)\,dt}$$

(5.6)

This is a mathematical model of the problem relating inspection schedule $x_1, x_2, x_3 \ldots$ to total cost per unit time $C(x_1, x_2, x_3, \ldots, x_k \ldots)$. The optimal schedule is the set of times $x_1, x_2, x_3 \ldots$ which minimizes the right-hand side of equation (5.6).

Basically, the optimal schedule is obtained by taking the partial derivative of $C(x_1, x_2, x_3 \ldots)$ with respect to x_k, for all values of $k = 1, 2, 3 \ldots$, equating to zero and then solving the resulting set of simultaneous equations.

5.5.3 SOLUTION PROCEDURE

Brender [7] (see also Barlow and Prochan [1]) gives the following procedure for obtaining a solution, in terms of the optimal schedule of inspection times.

Defining a residual function:

$$R(L; x_1, x_2, x_3 \ldots) = LE_i(x_1, x_2, x_3 \ldots) - E_c(x_1, x_2, x_3 \ldots)$$

(5.7)

where L represents either an initial estimation of the minimum cost $C(x_1, x_2, x_3 \ldots)$ or a value of $C(x_1, x_2, x_3 \ldots)$ obtained from a previous cycle of an iteration process.

Brender proves that the schedule $(x_1, x_2, x_3 \ldots)$ which maximizes $R(L: x_1, x_2, x_3 \ldots)$ is that schedule which minimizes $C(x_1, x_2, x_3 \ldots)$. The procedure for determining the optimal schedule is:

Step 1 Choose a value of L.

Step 2 Choose a value of x_1.

Step 3 Generate a schedule $x_1, x_2, x_3 \ldots$ using the recurrence relationship among the x_i (see below).

Step 4 Compute $R(L; x_1, x_2, x_3 \ldots)$ from equation (5.7).

Step 5 Repeat steps 2 to 4 with different values of x_1 until $R_{max}(L; x_1, x_2, x_3 \ldots)$ is obtained.

Step 6 Repeat steps 1 to 5 with different values of L until $R_{max}(L; x_1, x_2, x_3 \ldots) = 0$.

A procedure for adjusting L until it is identical with the minimum cost can be obtained from:

$$C(L; x_1, x_2, x_3 \ldots) = L - \frac{R_{max}(L; x_1, x_2, x_3 \ldots)}{E_l(x_1, x_2, x_3 \ldots)}$$

The recurrence relationship among the x_i is

$$x_{i+1} = x_i + \frac{F(x_i) - F(x_{i-1})}{f(x_i)} - \frac{C_i}{C_u - L} \tag{5.8}$$

5.5.4 NUMERICAL EXAMPLE
The following is taken from Brender's paper [7].

The failure distribution is assumed to be a gamma distribution* with $k = 3$ and mean μ. Defining μ as 1000 hours, $C_i = \$150$, $C_u = \$3$, $C_r = \$2000$ the optimal inspection schedule, for the first four points is determined as

$$x_1 = 947 \text{ hours} \qquad x_2 = 1442 \text{ hours}$$
$$x_3 = 1889 \text{ hours} \qquad x_4 = 2313 \text{ hours}$$

The corresponding minimal total cost per hour equals $2·44.

5.5.5 FURTHER COMMENTS
The approach taken in the inspection problem of this section can be applied to equipment which is not in continuous use, but which is perhaps stored for use in emergency conditions and, if found defective when called in to use, or at inspection, it is returned to the as new condition through maintenance. Rather than determine an inspection schedule to minimize total cost the appropriate objective may be "maximize the proportion of time equipment is in an available (or good) state".

A possible extension of the model covered here would be the inclusion of some form of preventive maintenance occurring at specific points in time.

---

* The gamma distribution is a family of curves whose form depends on the value of the shaping parameter k which is an integer. When $k = 1$ it takes the negative exponential form; when $k > 1$ it approaches the normal distribution. For the gamma distribution,

$$f(t) = \frac{\alpha(\alpha k)^{k-1} \exp[-\alpha t]}{(k-1)!}$$

where $\alpha = 1/b$, b is a scale parameter. The mean of the distribution, $\mu = kb$.

6 Overhaul and Repair Decisions

6.1 Introduction

In this chapter an overhaul is taken to be a restorative maintenance action which is taken before equipment has reached a defined failed state, while a repair is made after the failed state has occurred. (Note that the failed state does not necessarily mean that equipment has "broken-down" in the usual sense that it ceases completely to function, but it may be in a failed state because items, say, are being produced outside specific tolerance limits.)

The main problems associated with overhauling and repairing are determination of:

(a) The interval between overhauls. Note that this could be infinity which means that no overhauls (i.e. a form of preventive maintenance) but only repairs are made (i.e. breakdown maintenance); and

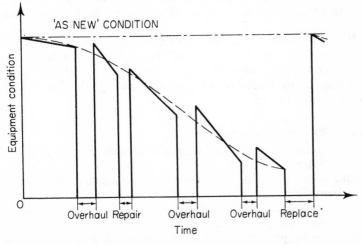

Fig. 6.1

(b) The degree to which equipment should be overhauled or repaired, i.e. just how close to the as new condition does the equipment get as a result of maintenance. (Note that in the limit both overhaul and repair could be equivalent to replacement.)

Figure 6.1 illustrates the "usual" consequences of overhauls and repairs. Thus it is seen that they both improve the condition of the equipment but there is a gradual deterioration over time and then replacement of the complete equipment is made. (See Chapter 4 for methods of determining when replacement should occur, especially Sections 4.6 to 4.9.)

When overhaul or repair can be taken to be equivalent to replacement, as is often the case in practice, then the models of Chapter 4 can be used. In this chapter the problems discussed are ones where maintenance in the form of overhaul or repair does not return equipment to the as new condition. The possibility of replacing will be included as a possible alternative along with overhaul and/or repair.

6.2 Optimal overhaul/repair/replace maintenance policy for equipment subject to breakdown: finite time horizon

6.2.1 STATEMENT OF PROBLEM

Equipment is subject to failure. On failure, one of two possible actions can be taken: repair or complete replacement of the failed equipment. To reduce the frequency of failure, preventive maintenance can be adopted; thus at various points in time the decision can be taken to overhaul the equipment or replace it while it is still in an operating state.

It will be assumed that decisions can only be made at discrete points in time (e.g., every weekend) and we wish to determine a decision rule which tells us which action to take at each decision point to minimize the total cost of maintenance and lost production over the next n periods of time.

6.2.2. CONSTRUCTION OF MODEL

(1) I is the state of the equipment (in this case good or failed) at the start of a period.
(2) J is the state of the equipment (good or failed) at the end of a period.
(3) a is the action which is taken at the start of a period (in this case overhaul, repair or replace).
(4) p_{IJ}^a is the probability that the equipment will go from state I to J in one period if action a is taken.

(5) C_{IJ}^a is the cost per period of going from state I to J if action a is taken. (In this case this will be the cost of overhaul C_O, repair C_r, or replacement C_R, and a cost C_l associated with lost production if equipment fails during the period.)

(6) The objective is to determine a combined overhaul/repair/ replace policy to minimize the total cost associated with these actions, and any consequential production losses, over the next n periods of time.

The minimal expected total cost, with n periods to go and starting in state I, is $f_n(I)$.

The cost of the first decision, at the start of the nth period, is C_{IJ}^a if action a is taken and we result in state J. But we would only result in state J with probability p_{IJ}^a. There are a number of results that could occur if action a is taken, therefore the expected cost resulting from action a is

$$\sum_{J=1}^{N} C_{IJ}^a \, p_{IJ}^a$$

where N is the number of possible states at the end of a period.

At the end of the period we are in state J, with $(n-1)$ periods to operate. The minimal total expected cost over this remaining time is $f_{n-1}(J)$. Again, we are only in state J with probability p_{IJ}^a and therefore expected cost is

$$\sum_{J=1}^{N} p_{IJ}^a f_{n-1}(J)$$

Thus, starting in state I, with n periods to go, taking action a and resulting in state J, the expected total cost over the n periods is

$$\text{Expected cost of first decision} + \text{Expected future costs} = \sum_{J=1}^{N} C_{IJ}^a \, p_{IJ}^a + \sum_{J=1}^{N} p_{IJ}^a f_{n-1}(J) \tag{6.1}$$

Since we wish to minimize the expected total cost we wish to take the best action a when in state I with n periods to go. The best action is that one which minimizes equation (6.1). The resulting minimal total expected cost $f_n(I)$ and best action a can be obtained from the following recurrence relation:

$$f_n(I) = \min_a \left[\sum_{J=1}^{N} C_{IJ}^a \, p_{IJ}^a + \sum_{J=1}^{N} p_{IJ}^a f_{n-1}(J) \right] \quad n \geqslant 1 \tag{6.2}$$

Note that equation (6.2) is almost the same as equations (4.7) and (4.8) of Chapter 4 except that, in this case, probabilities are included in the analysis.

Equation (6.2) can be solved recursively with the starting condition $f_0(I) = 0$, then

$$f_1(I) = \min_a \left[\sum_{J=1}^{N} C_{IJ}^a \, p_{IJ}^a \right] \qquad \text{etc.} \qquad (6.3)$$

The solution procedure will be illustrated in the following example.

6.2.3 NUMERICAL EXAMPLE

With reference to Figure 6.2 where the circles represent possible conditions of the equipment at the time of making a decision and the

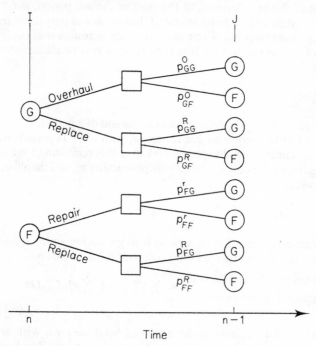

Fig. 6.2

squares represent the occurrence or non-occurrence of the event equipment failure, we see that:

(1) There are two possible conditions of the equipment at the start of a period, i.e. $I = $ Good (G) or Failed (F). Also, J the condition at the end of the period is G or F.
(2) There are three possible actions which can be taken, i.e. $a = $ overhaul (O), repair (r), replace (R).

(3) If the equipment is in condition G it can either be overhauled (O) or replaced (R). If overhauled, then there is a probability p_{GG}^O that the equipment will still be good at the end of the period, and a probability p_{GF}^O that it will have failed.

If the decision to replace is taken the probabilities are p_{GG}^R and p_{GF}^R that the equipment will be good or failed at the end of the period.

If equipment is in condition F, then it can either be repaired or replaced. The appropriate transition probabilities are given in Table 6.1, depending on whether or not failure occurs before the end of the period.

Table 6.1

Condition at start of period	Decision	Condition at end of period	
		Good	Failed
Good	Overhaul	$p_{GG}^O = 0.75$	$p_{GF}^O = 0.25$
	Replace	$p_{GG}^R = 0.95$	$p_{GF}^R = 0.05$
Failed	Repair	$p_{FG}^r = 0.60$	$p_{FF}^r = 0.40$
	Replace	$p_{FG}^R = 0.95$	$p_{FF}^R = 0.05$

(4) The cost per period C_{IJ}^a is given in Table 6.2.

Table 6.2

Condition at start of period	Decision	Condition at end of period	
		Good	Failed
Good	Overhaul	$C_{GG}^O = £200$	$C_{GF}^O = £1\,200$
	Replace	$C_{GG}^R = £500$	$C_{GF}^R = £1\,500$
Failed	Repair	$C_{FG}^r = £100$	$C_{FF}^r = £1\,100$
	Replace	$C_{FG}^R = £500$	$C_{FF}^R = £1\,500$

Thus it is seen that if equipment is good at start of period and it is overhauled the total cost incurred in the period is £200 (i.e. the overhaul cost), whereas if it fails during the period the cost is

£1 200 (i.e. it is a cost made up of the overhaul cost plus lost production).

(5) The objective is to determine the optimal maintenance policy such that the expected total cost over four future periods of time is minimized. Figure 6.3 shows the appropriate probabili-

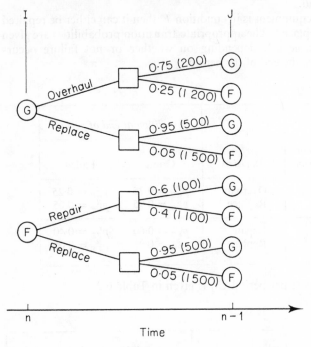

Fig. 6.3

ties and costs associated with the alternative decisions. Thus it is seen that if the equipment is good (*G*) at the start of the period there is a probability of 0·75 that the equipment will be in condition *G* at the end of the period and the resulting cost is £200 (the overhaul cost). If the equipment fails the cost is £1 200 (made up of £200 for overhaul, plus £1 000 for lost production) and the probability of this occurring is 0·25.

Equation (6.3) is

$$f_1(I) = \frac{\min}{a} \left[\sum_{J=1}^{N} C_{IJ}^a p_{IJ}^a \right]$$

When $I = G$, with one period to go, there are two possible maintenance actions:

$$f_1(G) = \min \begin{bmatrix} \sum_{J=1}^{N} C_{GJ}^{O} p_{GJ}^{O} & \text{overhaul} \\ \sum_{J=1}^{N} C_{GJ}^{R} p_{GJ}^{R} & \text{replace} \end{bmatrix}$$

Consider the decision to overhaul, then:

$$\sum_{J=1}^{N} C_{GJ}^{O} p_{GJ}^{O} = C_{GG}^{O} p_{GG}^{O} + C_{GF}^{O} p_{GF}^{O}$$
$$= 200(0.75) + 1\,200(0.25) = \text{£}450$$

Consider the decision to replace, then:

$$\sum_{J=1}^{N} C_{GJ}^{R} p_{GJ}^{R} = C_{GG}^{R} p_{GG}^{R} + C_{GF}^{R} p_{GF}^{R}$$
$$= 500(0.95) + 1\,500(0.05) = \text{£}550$$

Thus

$$f_1(G) = \min \begin{bmatrix} 450 \\ 550 \end{bmatrix} = \text{£}450$$

and so the best decision for minimizing total expected future cost is to overhaul.

When $I = F$, with one period to go:

$$f_1(F) = \min \begin{bmatrix} \sum_{J=1}^{N} C_{FJ}^{r} p_{FJ}^{r} & \text{repair} \\ \sum_{J=1}^{N} C_{FJ}^{R} p_{FJ}^{R} & \text{replace} \end{bmatrix}$$

$$= \min \begin{bmatrix} 100(0.6) + 1\,100(0.4) \\ 500(0.95) + 1\,500(0.05) \end{bmatrix}$$

$$= \min \begin{bmatrix} 500 \\ 550 \end{bmatrix} = \text{£}500$$

and so the best decision for minimizing total expected future cost is to repair.

With two periods of time to go equation (6.2) becomes:

$$f_2(I) = \min_{a} \left[\sum_{J=1}^{N} C_{IJ}^{a} p_{IJ}^{a} + \sum_{J=1}^{N} p_{IJ}^{a} f_1(J) \right]$$

When $I = G$, with two periods to go:

$$f_2(G) = \min \begin{bmatrix} C_{GG}^O p_{GG}^O + C_{GF}^O p_{GF}^O + p_{GG}^O f_1(G) + p_{GF}^O f_1(F) \\ C_{GG}^R p_{GG}^R + C_{GF}^R p_{GF}^R + p_{GG}^R f_1(G) + p_{GF}^R f_1(F) \end{bmatrix} \begin{array}{l} \text{overhaul} \\ \text{replace} \end{array}$$

$$= \min \begin{bmatrix} 450 + 450(0\cdot75) + 500(0\cdot25) \\ 550 + 450(0\cdot95) + 500(0\cdot05) \end{bmatrix}$$

$$= \min \begin{bmatrix} 912\cdot5 \\ 1\,002\cdot5 \end{bmatrix}$$

$= £912\cdot5$ and so the best decision is to overhaul.

When $I = F$, with two periods to go:

$$f_2(F) = \min \begin{bmatrix} 970\cdot0 \\ 1\,002\cdot5 \end{bmatrix} \begin{array}{l} \text{repair} \\ \text{replace} \end{array}$$

$= £970$ and so the best decision is to repair.

Proceeding with the calculations in a similar manner to the above, Table 6.3 can be constructed for values of n up to 4. Thus it is seen that if there are 4 periods to go and equipment is in condition good (G), the best decision is to overhaul and the resulting expected future costs is £1 841·6. Similarly the best decision at any point in time can be identified from the table. Note that in the example the best decision is always to overhaul if the equipment is in state G at the start of a period and to repair if it is in state F. This result is due solely to the costs and probabilities used in the example and may be different for other cost and probability patterns.

Table 6.3

Periods to go: n	4		3		2		1	
State of equipment at start of period: I	G	F	G	F	G	F	G	F
Action to take at start of period	Overhaul	Repair	Overhaul	Repair	Overhaul	Repair	Overhaul	Repair
Expected future cost: $f_n(I)$	1841·6	1900·3	1376·9	1435·5	912·5	970	450	500

6.2.4 FURTHER COMMENTS

In this section the criterion used to determine the best maintenance policy was total cost. Other criteria such as downtime or profit could equally well have been used in the analysis. If a downtime criterion was relevant then of course the times required to effect overhaul, repair or replacement would have to be included in the analysis. In the example of this section these times were neglected. This, of course, is not unreasonable if they are short relative to the usual operating period of the equipment or if they can be done at weekends, say, when the equipment is not used.

In practice, the period of time over which we wish to optimize our maintenance decisions may be very long and so we may be interested in determining what the best decisions are and what the resulting cost is when the period *n* tends to infinity. This aspect will be covered in the following section where it will be seen that decisions depend only on the condition of the equipment, and not on how long it has still to run to the planning horizon.

The problem of this section assumed that a decision had to be made at every period. Problems can arise when it is necessary to determine when the next decision is to be taken, knowing that a failure may force us to take some maintenance action before the planned time. Thus, if we make a decision to overhaul plant we may also decide that the next time a decision will be taken (either to overhaul or replace) will be after *n* future periods of time, or earlier if the equipment fails, when the alternatives may be repair, or replace. Construction of a model for this problem is given by White [48].

In the example of this section it was assumed that the condition of the equipment could be specified by being either good (*G*) or failed (*F*) and the relevant transition probabilities were those of going from condition *G* to *F* under various maintenance actions. In many maintenance problems it may be necessary to describe the condition more specifically. For example, as well as knowing whether or not equipment is good, we may also wish to know how long it has been in operation since the previous maintenance action. Also, alternatives other than overhaul, repair and replace may need to be considered. Further alternatives might include "do nothing", and/or may result from the wish to specify various degrees to which the equipment can be overhauled. Inclusion of such further alternatives can be handled in the manner outlined in this section. Tackling such a problem would result in a larger matrix of transition probabilities where, for example, the transition probabilities after overhaul may depend on the age of the equipment when the overhaul was started, or they may depend on the level of the overhaul.

6.3 Optimal overhaul/repair/replace maintenance policy for equipment subject to breakdown: infinite time horizon

6.3.1 STATEMENT OF PROBLEM

The problem is almost identical to that of the previous section (6.2.1) except that we wish to determine the optimal maintenance policy over

a long period of time and therefore we will minimize expected total
cost per unit time, rather than over n future periods of time.

6.3.2 CONSTRUCTION OF MODEL

(1) The parameters I, J, a, p_{IJ}^a, C_{IJ}^a and N and are as defined for the
    previous problem (Section 6.2.2).

(2) The objective is to determine a combined overhaul/repair/
    replace policy to minimize the expected total cost associated
    with these actions, and any consequential production losses,
    over a long period of time. Thus we wish to minimize expected
    total cost per unit time.

Letting $f_n(I)$ be the minimal total expected cost over the next n
periods of time then, as $n \to \infty$,

$$f_n(I) \to ng + v(I)$$

where g may be interpreted as the long-run average gain per period (or
cost, profit, etc., depending on the problem) and $v(I)$ is a cost which
depends on the state of the equipment at the start of operation, i.e.
$f_n(I)$ is composed of two parts—a steady state part ng and a transient
part $v(I)$ which depends on the starting state.

Therefore for sufficiently large n,

$$f_n(I) = \min_a \left[\sum_{J=1}^{N} C_{IJ}^a p_{IJ}^a + \sum_{J=1}^{N} p_{IJ}^a f_{n-1}(J) \right] \quad \text{(from equation 6.2)}$$

$$= ng + v(I)$$

Now $f_{n-1}(J) = (n-1)g + v(J)$ and therefore

$$ng + v(I) = \min_a \left[\sum_{J=1}^{N} C_{IJ}^a p_{IJ}^a + \sum_{J=1}^{N} p_{IJ}^a (n-1)g + \sum_{J=1}^{N} p_{IJ}^a v(J) \right]$$

i.e. $$g + v(I) = \min_a \left[\sum_{J=1}^{N} C_{IJ}^a p_{IJ}^a + \sum_{J=1}^{N} p_{IJ}^a v(J) \right] \quad (6.4)$$

since $\sum_{J=1}^{N} p_{IJ}^a = 1$.

Expression (6.4) is a system of N equations in $N + 1$ unknowns (the
N $v(I)$'s plus g). (Note: N is the number of possible states.)

Solution of (6.4) can be obtained by using the following algorithm
developed by Howard [22].

(i) Choose some policy (arbitrarily).

(ii) If there are N possible states, let $v(N) = 0$.

(iii) Solve the N equations of expression (6.4) to give the average long-term gain g and the relative values $v(I)$ of various starting states.

(iv) For each condition, I, and using the $v(I)$ values obtained in step (iii), find the alternative, a, which optimizes (maximizes or minimizes depending on objective):

$$\sum_{J=1}^{N} C_{IJ}^{a} p_{IJ}^{a} + \sum_{J=1}^{N} p_{IJ}^{a} v(J) \qquad (6.5)$$

(v) Using the policy obtained in step (iv) repeat at step (iii) until the optimal policy is determined. This is specified when g is maximized (or minimized) and will be the case when the policies on two successive iterations are identical.

6.3.3 NUMERICAL EXAMPLE

Using the transition probabilities and costs used in the previous example (Section 6.2.3) determine the optimal maintenance policy and long run average cost per period. The relevant data are given in Table 6.4.

Table 6.4

Condition at start of period	Decision	Condition at end of period G F Transition probabilities		Expected cost
G	Overhaul Replace	0·75 0·95	0·25 0·05	£450 £550
F	Repair Replace	0·60 0·95	0·40 0·05	£500 £550

Using Howard's algorithm we proceed as follows:

(i) Choose some policy. So, let us choose:

If in state G at start of period then replace.
If in state F at start of period then replace.

(ii) If there are N possible conditions, let $v(N) = 0$. In this example there are two possible conditions G and F, so let $v(F) = 0$.

(iii) Solve expression (6.4).
Expression (6.4) becomes

$$g + v(G) = 550 + 0.95\,v(G) + 0.05\,v(F)$$
$$g + v(F) = 550 + 0.95\,v(G) + 0.05\,v(F)$$

which gives $v(G) = 0$, $g = 550$ (solving the above two simultaneous equations).

(iv) For each condition find the best alternative using equation (6.5).

If in condition G, (6.5) becomes:

$$\min \begin{bmatrix} 450 + 0.75(0) + 0.25(0) \\ 550 + 0.95(0) + 0.05(0) \end{bmatrix}$$

$$= \min \begin{bmatrix} 450 \\ 550 \end{bmatrix} \leftarrow \text{minimum} \therefore \text{overhaul}$$

If in condition F, (6.5) becomes

$$\min \begin{bmatrix} 500 + 0.6(0) + 0.4(0) \\ 550 + 0.95(0) + 0.05(0) \end{bmatrix}$$

$$= \min \begin{bmatrix} 500 \\ 550 \end{bmatrix} \leftarrow \text{minimum} \therefore \text{repair}$$

Therefore at end of first iteration the new policy is:

If in condition G at start of period then overhaul.
If in condition F at start of period then repair.

(v) Using above policy solve expression (6.4) using $v(F) = 0$.
Expression (6.4) becomes

$$g + v(G) = 450 + 0.75\,v(G) + 0.25\,v(F)$$
$$g + v(F) = 500 + 0.6\,v(G) + 0.4\,v(F)$$

which gives $v(G) = -58.8$ and $g = 464.8$.

(vi) For each condition find best alternative using the values of $v(G)$ and g obtained in previous step, and using (6.5). If in condition G, (6.5) becomes

$$\min \begin{bmatrix} 450 + 0.75(-58.8) + 0.25(0) \\ 550 + 0.95(-58.8) + 0.05(0) \end{bmatrix}$$

$$= \min \begin{bmatrix} 405.9 \\ 494.1 \end{bmatrix} \leftarrow \text{minimum} \therefore \text{overhaul}$$

If in condition F, (6.5) becomes

$$\min \begin{bmatrix} 500 + 0\cdot6(-58\cdot8) + 0\cdot4(0) \\ 550 + 0\cdot95(-58\cdot8) + 0\cdot05(0) \end{bmatrix}$$

$$= \min \begin{bmatrix} 464\cdot7 \\ 494\cdot1 \end{bmatrix} \leftarrow\text{minimum} \therefore \text{repair}$$

Therefore, at end of second iteration the new policy is:

If in condition G at start of period then overhaul.
If in condition F at start of period then repair.

Thus the optimal decisions have been determined since the same policy has been obtained on two successive iterations. The resulting average cost per period is £464·7.

6.3.4 FURTHER COMMENTS
In the above example the time horizon is infinite. However, when the horizon over which we wish to optimize is finite then the best decision to take at any time may depend on the remaining number of periods the equipment is still required to operate.

6.4 Optimal overhaul cost limits for equipment

6.4.1 STATEMENT OF PROBLEM
When equipment is taken out of production, say, and sent to the maintenance workshops for overhaul, the decision frequently has to be taken, on the basis of estimated overhaul cost, whether to overhaul the equipment or replace it. The problem of this section is to determine optimal overhaul cost limits for equipment of different ages, faced with different overhaul cost estimates and where there is fixed future time over which equipment is required. The optimal control limits are determined to minimize the expected total cost of operation and overhaul over a fixed period of time. Thus if equipment, such as a vehicle, is sent for overhaul the decision on whether or not to overhaul is determined by comparing the estimated cost with the overhaul limit, i.e. the maximum amount of money which should be spent overhauling equipment of a given age.

6.4.2 CONSTRUCTION OF MODEL
(1) n is the number of periods equipment is still required to operate.
(2) I is the age of equipment at the beginning of a period.
(3) J is the age of the equipment at the end of a period. This will be $I + 1$ if the equipment was overhauled, otherwise $J = 1$ since it would have been replaced at the beginning of the period.

(4) $f_I(c)$ is the probability density function for the estimated overhaul cost c of equipment of age I.

(5) L_I is the overhaul cost limit for equipment of age I.

(6) $m_I(L_I)$ is the mean overhaul cost of equipment of age I with repair limit of L_I. Therefore

$$m_I(L_I) = \frac{\int_0^{L_I} cf_I(c)\,dc}{\int_0^{L_I} f_I(c)\,dc} \tag{6.6}$$

(cf. Section 4.11.2 where the mean time to failure $M(t_p)$ is calculated.)

(7) A is the acquisition cost of new equipment.

(8) $f_n(I)$ is the minimal expected total cost of replacing and overhauling equipment over n periods of time starting with equipment of age I.

(9) The objective is to determine overhaul limits L_I such that the minimal expected total cost $f_n(I)$ is obtained.

Figure 6.4 illustrates the problem. Thus it is seen that the overhaul cost c is estimated. There is a probability $p_{I,I+1}$ that the overhaul

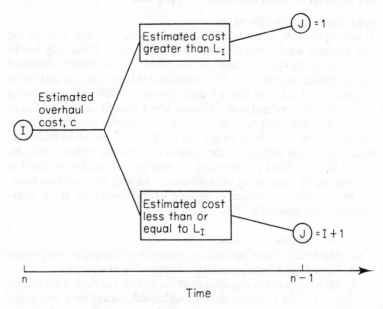

Fig. 6.4

cost will be less than or equal to the limit L_I, and a probability $p_{I,1}$ that the cost will exceed L_I. (Since if the overhaul limit is exceeded the equipment will be replaced, and then it is of age 1 at the end of the period. Thus we are assuming that the time required to effect an overhaul or replacement can be neglected.)

Defining $C_n(I, J)$ as the expected cost of the first decision with n periods still to operate and starting with equipment of age I we get:

$C_n(I, J)$ = Expected cost of overhaul
        × Probability that overhaul cost is less than overhaul limit
        + Cost of replacement
        × Probability that overhaul limit is exceeded

$$= m_I(L_I) \int_0^{L_I} f_I(c)\, dc + A \left(1 - \int_0^{L_I} f_I(c)\, dc \right)$$

Letting $\displaystyle\int_0^{L_I} f_I(c)\, dc = F_I(L)$ (6.7)

$$C_n(I, J) = m_I(L_I)F_I(L) + A[1 - F_I(L)]$$

Defining $f_{n-1}(J)$ as the minimal expected total cost over the remaining $(n - 1)$ periods:

$f_{n-1}(J)$ = Minimal future cost if equipment is of age $(I + 1)$
        × Probability that overhaul limit was not exceeded at time n
        + Minimal expected future cost if equipment is of age 1
        × Probability that overhaul limit was exceeded at time n
$$= f_{n-1}(I + 1)F_I(L) + f_{n-1}(1)[1 - F_I(L)]$$

Therefore the expected total cost over the remaining n periods starting with equipment of age I is

$$C_n(I, J) + f_{n-1}(J)$$

Since we wish to minimize this total cost by selection of appropriate overhaul limits we get the recurrence relation:

$$f_n(I) = \min_{L_I} \left[C_n(I, J) + f_{n-1}(J) \right]$$

$$= \min_{L_I} \left[m_I(L_I)F_I(L) + A[1 - F_I(L)] + f_{n-1}(I + 1)F_I(L) \right.$$

$$\left. + f_{n-1}(1)[1 - F_I(L)] \right] \qquad n \geqslant 1 \qquad (6.8)$$

with the starting condition that $f_0(I) = 0$ for all values of I.

6.4.3 NUMERICAL EXAMPLE

(1) The distribution of estimated overhaul costs for equipment of age 1 is rectangularly distributed (see Figure 4.29 for example) over range (0, 6).

When equipment is of age 2 the estimated overhaul costs are also rectangularly distributed, but over range (1, 7).

It will be assumed that equipment having age greater than 2 has the same estimated overhaul cost distribution as equipment of age 2, i.e. it is uniformly distributed over range (1, 7).

(2) The acquisition cost of new equipment is 7.

(3) The problem is to determine optimal overhaul cost limits over 2 periods of time.

From equation (6.8) we get, with 1 period to go:

$$f_1(I) = \frac{\min}{L_I} \left[m_I(L_I)F_I(L) + A[1 - F_1(L)] \right] \tag{6.9}$$

since $f_0(I + 1) = 0$ and $f_0(1) = 0$.

Assuming that the possible values of the control limits are 1, 2, 3, 4, 5 or 6 and letting $I = 1$ then equation (6.9) becomes

$$f_1(1) = \min \begin{bmatrix} m_1(1)F_1(1) + A[1 - F_1(1)] \\ m_1(2)F_1(2) + A[1 - F_1(2)] \\ \vdots \\ \vdots \\ m_1(6)F_1(6) + A[1 - F_1(6)] \end{bmatrix}$$

Now

$$m_1(1) = \frac{\int_0^1 c\frac{1}{6}\, dc}{\int_0^1 \frac{1}{6}\, dc} = \frac{1}{2} \qquad \text{(from equation 6.6)}$$

$$F_1(1) = \int_0^1 \tfrac{1}{6}\, dc = \tfrac{1}{6} \qquad \text{(from equation 6.7)}$$

Therefore $1 - F_1(1) = \frac{5}{6}$.

Similarly $m_1(2) \ldots m_1(6)$ and $F_1(2) \ldots F_1(6)$ can be calculated. This then gives

$$f_1(1) = \min \begin{bmatrix} \frac{1}{2} \times \frac{1}{6} + 7 \times \frac{5}{6} \\ 1 \times \frac{1}{3} + 7 \times \frac{2}{3} \\ 1\frac{1}{2} \times \frac{1}{2} + 7 \times \frac{1}{2} \\ 2 \times \frac{2}{3} + 7 \times \frac{1}{3} \\ 2\frac{1}{2} \times \frac{5}{6} + 7 \times \frac{1}{6} \\ 3 \times 1 + 7 \times 0 \end{bmatrix} = \min \begin{bmatrix} 5\frac{11}{12} \\ 5\cdot0 \\ 4\frac{1}{4} \\ 3\frac{2}{3} \\ 3\frac{1}{4} \\ 3\cdot0 \end{bmatrix}$$

Therefore $f_1(1) = 3 \cdot 0$ which occurs when the overhaul limit is 6. Thus the decision will always be to overhaul equipment of age 1 when there is one period to run.

Proceeding in the above manner when $I = 2$, with 1 period to go, $f_1(2) = 4 \cdot 0$ and this occurs when the overhaul limit is $7 \cdot 0$. (Note that when $I = 2$ the possible values of the overhaul limit are 2, 3, 4, 5, 6 or 7.)

This information can now be summarized in Table 6.5,

Table 6.5

Age of equipment at start of period I	1	2
Overhaul limit L_I	6	7
Minimum total expected cost $f_1(I)$	3·0	4·0

When there are 2 periods to go, then equation (6.8) becomes

$$f_2(I) = \min_{L_I} \left[m_I(L)F_I(L) + A[1 - F_I(L)] + f_1(I+1)F_I(L) \right.$$
$$\left. + f_1(1)[1 - F_1 L)] \right] \qquad (6.10)$$

If $I = 1$, and the possible overhaul limits are 1, 2, 3, 4, 5 and 6, then from equation (6.10) we get

$$f_2(1) = \min \begin{bmatrix} m_1(1)F_1(1) + A[1 - F_1(1)] \\ \quad + f_1(2)F_1(1) + f_1(1)[1 - F_1(1)] \\ m_1(2)F_1(2) + A[1 - F_1(2)] \\ \quad + f_1(2)F_1(2) + f_1(1)[1 - F_1(2)] \\ \cdot \\ \cdot \\ \cdot \\ m_1(6)F_1(6) + A[1 - F_1(6)] \\ \quad + f_1(2)F_1(6) + f_1(1)[1 - F_1(6)] \end{bmatrix}$$

$$= \min \begin{bmatrix} 5\frac{11}{12} + 4 \times \frac{1}{6} + 3 \times \frac{5}{6} \\ 5 + 4 \times \frac{1}{3} + 3 \times \frac{2}{3} \\ 4 + 4 \times \frac{1}{2} + 3 \times \frac{1}{2} \\ 3\frac{2}{3} + 4 \times \frac{2}{3} + 3 \times \frac{1}{3} \\ 3\frac{1}{4} + 4 \times \frac{5}{6} + 3 \times \frac{1}{6} \\ 3 + 4 \times 1 + 3 \times 0 \end{bmatrix} = \min \begin{bmatrix} 9\frac{1}{6} \\ 8\frac{1}{3} \\ 7\frac{3}{4} \\ 7\frac{1}{3} \\ 7\frac{1}{2} \\ 7 \end{bmatrix}$$

Therefore $f_2(1) = 7$ and this occurs when the overhaul limit is 6.

Proceeding as above when $I = 2$, with 2 periods to go, $f_2(2) = 7\frac{11}{12}$ and this occurs when the repair limit is 6.

Table 6.6

Age of equipment at start of period I	1	2
Overhaul limit L_I	6	6
Minimum total expected cost $f_2(I)$	7	$7\frac{11}{12}$

Thus, for example, from Table 6.6 we see that if equipment is of age 2, with 2 periods to go, and if the estimated overhaul cost is less than 6, then it should be overhauled; if greater than 6 (it could be up to 7) then it should be replaced. If the repair cost equals 6 then we could be indifferent to overhauling and replacing and either decisions could equally well be taken.

6.4.4 FURTHER COMMENTS

In the model of this section it was assumed that overhauls occurred at regular intervals and we have also assumed that the estimated overhaul cost was equal to the actual cost incurred. Hastings [20] extends the ideas of this section to cater for failures occurring and when such a failure occurs an estimate of the repair cost is made. Hastings used a recurrence relation similar to equation (6.8) to determine optimal repair limits.

Although the analysis of the example of this section was only carried out for 2 periods ($n = 2$) it could easily be extended to cater for larger values of n. If n is assumed to be large then the infinite planning horizon approach of Section 6.3 is appropriate. Such an extension is also covered by Hastings.

7 Organizational Structure Decisions

7.1 Introduction

The two interrelated problem areas, concerning what type of maintenance organization should exist, which will be considered in this chapter are:

(i) Determination of what facilities (e.g. manpower and equipment) there should be within an organization; and
(ii) Determination of how these facilities should be used, taking into account the possible use of subcontractors (i.e. outside resources).

THE FACILITIES FOR MAINTENANCE WITHIN AN ORGANIZATION

Within an organization there are generally some maintenance facilities available such as workshops, stores and manpower. In addition there is usually some form of contact between the organization and contractors who are capable of performing some or all of the maintenance work required by the organization.

The problem is to determine the "best" composition of facilities for maintenance. Increase in the range of maintenance equipment, such as lathes, increases the capital tied up in plant and buildings and require an increase in manpower. Increases in the in-plant facilities, however, will reduce the need to use outside resources such as general engineering workshops. In this case a balance is required between costs associated with using in-plant facilities and costs of using outside resources. A difficult costing problem arises since not only does the cost charged by the outside resource have to be considered, but also the cost associated with loss of control of maintenance work by management. For example, by using outside resources there is the possibility of greater downtime occurring on production equipment and so a cost must be associated with this downtime.

Also within this area there is the problem of determining the size of the maintenance crew. The major conflicts arising here are that:

(i) As crew size increases, so does its cost.
(ii) As crew size increases, the time which machines are idle waiting on a crewman decreases.

(iii) Downtime may be reduced since larger crews can be used to repair equipment.

THE COMBINED USE OF THE FACILITIES WITHIN AN ORGANIZATION
AND OUTSIDE RESOURCES

Maintenance work can be performed by either company personnel or contractors, on company premises or in contractors' workshops. Just which of these alternatives are invoked at any particular time will depend upon:

(i) the nature of the maintenance work required,
(ii) the maintenance facilities available within the company,
(iii) the workload on these facilities,
(iv) the costs associated with the various alternatives.

It should be noted that these alternatives are not mutually exclusive since maintenance work (e.g. the repair of a piece of equipment) can be done by cooperation between the company's facilities and outside resources.

7.2 Queueing theory preliminaries

Since the problems of Sections 7.3 to 7.6 use results obtained from the mathematical theory of queues (or waiting line theory) we will first give a brief introduction to the relevant aspects of this theory.

Queueing theory deals with problems of congestion where "customers" arrive at a service facility, perhaps wait in a queue, are served by "servers", and then leave the service facility. In maintenance problems customers may take the form of jobs arriving at a workshop from various production facilities, breakdowns occurring in a group of machines, and the servers in these cases could be the lathes in the workshop and the maintenance crews available to look after machine breakdowns. The results of queueing theory enable questions such as the following to be answered:

For a given service facility (e.g. workshop size, maintenance crew size) what is the average time that a job has to wait in a queue?

For a given service facility what is the average number of jobs in the system at any one time?

For a given service facility and given pattern of workload, what is the average idle time of the facility?

For a given service facility, what is the probability of a waiting time greater than t?

For a given service facility what is the probability of one of the servers in the facility being idle?

Once information such as the above is obtained it may then be possible to identify the optimal size of the service facility to minimize the total cost of the service facility and downtime incurred due to jobs waiting in a queue for service. These basic conflicts are illustrated in Figure 7.1

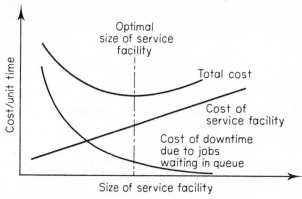

Fig. 7.1

7.2.1 QUEUEING SYSTEMS

Figures 7.2(*a*) and (*b*) depict the usual queueing systems we deal with. Figure 7.2(*a*) is the situation where there is a single server facility (i.e. single channel) and only one customer can be served at any time. All incoming jobs join a queue, unless the service facility is idle, and eventually depart from the system.

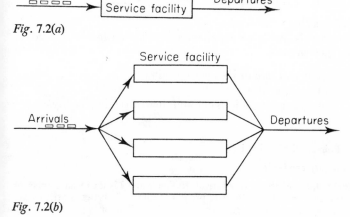

Fig. 7.2(*a*)

Fig. 7.2(*b*)

Figure 7.2(*b*) is a multi-channel system where customers join a queue and then go from the queue to the first service facility that becomes vacant.

Before analysis of a queueing system can be undertaken the following information must be obtained:

(*a*) *The arrival pattern of customers.* In this chapter the arrival pattern will be assumed to be random, i.e. the interval between the arrival of jobs at the service facility will be negative exponentially distributed. Thus we are dealing with a Poisson process where the arrival rate per unit time is distributed according to the Poisson distribution.*

(*b*) *The service pattern of the facility.* In this chapter the service distribution is assumed to be negative exponential, i.e. the time taken to repair a job in the service facility is negative exponentially distributed.

(*c*) *The priority rules.* In this chapter the priority rule is: customers are served (or begin service) in the order of their arrival.

In practice, the assumptions made in (*a*), (*b*) and (*c*) are often acceptable although other patterns of arrival or service, or priority rule, may be appropriate. When this is the case then the general results of queueing theory used in the chapter may not be applicable and the reader will have to seek guidance in some of the standard references to queueing theory (see [26] and [13]).

When dealing with complex queueing situations it is often the case that analytical solution cannot be obtained and in this case we may resort to simulation. This will be covered in the problem of Section 7.5.

7.2.2 QUEUEING THEORY RESULTS

Single channel queueing system
Poisson arrivals, negative exponential service, customers served in order of their arrival.

$\quad\lambda$ mean arrival rate of jobs per unit time
$1/\lambda$ mean time between arrivals
$\quad\mu$ mean service rate of jobs per unit time (if serving facility is kept busy)

---

* The Poisson distribution is

$$P(r) = (\lambda t)^r \exp\left[-\lambda t\right]/r!$$

where $P(r)$ is the probability of r arrivals in time t and λ is the mean number of arrivals per unit time. For a Poisson process the intervals between arrivals are distributed according to the negative exponential distribution.

Then we can calculate the following statistics which apply in the "steady state", i.e., the system has settled down:

Mean waiting time of a job in the system $W_s = 1/(\mu - \lambda)$

Mean time one job waits in a queue $W_q = \rho/(\mu - \lambda)$

where ρ is termed the traffic intensity $= \lambda/\mu$.

Note that to ensure that an infinite queue does not build up ρ must always be less than 1. The above results for W_s and W_q depend on this assumption.

Multi-channel queueing systems

Although formulae are available for waiting times, etc., in certain multi-channel systems, with particular arrival and service patterns,

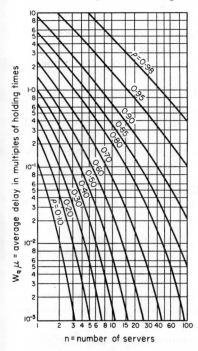

Fig. 7.3

they are beyond the scope of this book. However, tables and charts are available which enable us to obtain directly the quantities we need. Such tables include those of Peck and Hazelwood [37]. The chart of Figure 7.3, which is taken from Wilkinson [51], is used to determine the mean waiting time of a job in the system. A similar chart appears in Morse [33], as do charts of other queueing statistics.

7.3 Optimal number of workshop machines to meet a fluctuating workload

7.3.1 STATEMENT OF PROBLEM

From time to time jobs requiring the use of workshop machines (say lathes) are sent from various production facilities within an organization to the maintenance workshop. Depending on the workload of the workshop these jobs will be returned to production after some time has elapsed. The problem is to determine the optimal number of machines which minimizes the total cost of the system. This cost has two components: the cost of the workshop facilities and the cost of downtime incurred due to jobs waiting in the workshop queue and then being repaired.

7.3.2 CONSTRUCTION OF MODEL

(1) The arrival rate of jobs to the workshop requiring work on a lathe is Poisson distributed with arrival rate λ.

(2) The service time a job requires on a lathe is negative exponentially distributed with mean $1/\mu$.

(3) The downtime cost per unit time for a job waiting in the system (i.e. being served or in the queue) is C_d.

(4) The cost of operation per unit time for one lathe (either operating or idle) is C_l.

(5) The objective is to determine the optimal number of lathes n to minimize the total cost per unit time $C(n)$ of the system.

$C(n) =$ Cost per unit time of the lathes
    $+$ Downtime cost per unit time due to jobs being in the system

Cost per unit time of the lathes $=$ Number of lathes
    $\times$ Cost per unit time per lathe
    $= nC_l$

Downtime cost per unit time of jobs being in the system $=$ Average wait in the system per job
    $\times$ Arrival rate of jobs in the system per unit time
    $\times$ Downtime cost per unit time/job
    $= W_s \lambda C_d$

where $W_s =$ mean wait of a job in the system. Hence

$$C(n) = nC_l + W_s \lambda C_d \tag{7.1}$$

This is a model of the problem relating number of machines n to total cost $C(n)$.

7.3.3 NUMERICAL EXAMPLE

Letting $\lambda = 30$ jobs/week, $\mu = 5.5$ jobs/week (for one lathe), C_d £500/week, $C_l = £200$/week then equation (7.1) can be evaluated for different numbers of lathes to give Table 7.1. Thus it is seen that the optimal number of lathes to minimize total cost per week is 8.

Table 7.1

Number of lathes, n	Mean wait of a job in the system, W_s	Total cost per week, $C(n)$
6	0·437	7755
7	0·237	4955
8	0·198	4570
9	0·189	4635
10	0·185	4775
11	0·183	4945
12	0·182	5130

Figure 7.4 illustrates the underlying pattern of downtime and lathe costs which when added together give the total costs of Table 7.1.

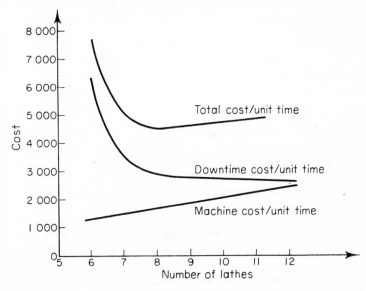

Fig. 7.4

It is also interesting to plot Figure 7.5 which gives the average idle time and busy time per week for each lathe for different numbers of lathes. Note that when $n = 8$, the optimal number from a total cost viewpoint, average idle time of a lathe is 32%, i.e. utilization is 68%. So often the comment is made that a high utilization for equipment is required and only then is it being operated efficiently. In some cases

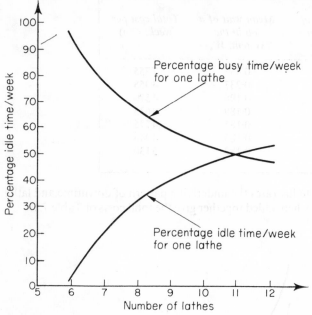

Fig. 7.5

this will be so but we see from this example that if the utilization of a lathe were increased from 68% to 91% (which would occur when $n = 6$) the total cost per week would increase from £4570 to £7750. Again the point can be made that we must be clear in our mind what objective we are trying to achieve in our maintenance decisions.

Sample calculations
When $n = 1$ to 5, then $\rho = \lambda/n\mu$, the traffic intensity, is greater than 1. Thus an infinite queue will eventually build up since work is arriving faster than it can be processed and so we consider cases of n at least equal to 6. (Note that the formulae apply to the steady state. In practice an infinite queue cannot be formed.)

From Figure 7.3, when $n = 6, \rho = 0.91$ then $W_q\mu = 1.4$. Therefore
Mean wait in a queue $W_q = 1.4(0.182) = 0.255$ week

Therefore

$$W_s = W_q + \text{mean service time} = 0.255 + 0.182 = 0.437 \text{ week}$$

From equation (7.1),

$$C(6) = 6 \times 200 + 0.437 \times 30 \times 500 = 1200 + 6555 = \pounds 7755$$

To calculate the average busy time per week for one lathe:

Average busy time per week = Average number of jobs to lathe per
week
× Average time of one job on a lathe

$$= \frac{\lambda}{n} \times \frac{1}{\mu}$$

Therefore

Average idle time per week $= 1 - \dfrac{\lambda}{n\mu}$

When $n = 6, \lambda = 30, \mu = 5.5$, then

Average busy time per week for one lathe $= 30/(6 \times 5.5) = 0.91$
Average idle time per week for one lathe $= 1 - 0.91 = 0.09$

Note that ρ, the traffic intensity, is in fact equivalent to the average busy time per week.

7.3.4 FURTHER COMMENTS

The method of tackling the lathe problem of this section is the same as that which could be adopted to determine the optimal size of a maintenance crew. In that case the number of men in the crew corresponds to the number of machines in the lathe group. One report of such a study is that of Carruthers *et al.* [9].

In the problem of this section it was assumed that all the machines were the same, and any machine could equally well be used for any job requiring lathe work. This may not be the case. For example, within a group of lathes there may be "small", "medium" and "large" lathes. Certain incoming jobs may be done equally well on any of the lathes, but others may only be processed on, say, a large lathe. This sort of problem will be discussed, and analysed in more detail in Section 7.5.

Further, in this section it was assumed that all of the workload was processed on workshop machines which were internal to the organization. In many situations advantage can be taken of subcontractors to do some of the work during busy periods. The approach used in Section 7.7 to determine the optimal size of a maintenance crew, taking account of subcontracting opportunities, can, in particular cases, be used to determine the optimal number of workshop machines where subcontracting opportunities occur.

7.4 Optimal repair effort of a repair crew

7.4.1 STATEMENT OF PROBLEM

There is one repair crew whose rate of work can be influenced at a cost, such as by the provision of portable equipment or by bonus payments. The crew is responsible for the maintenance of a group of machines. If a machine breaks down and the repair crew is idle, then attention is given to the machine immediately, otherwise it waits in a queue until attended to by the crew. When a machine is waiting in the queue or being repaired by the crew there is a loss of production and the problem is to determine the best rate of work of the crew to minimize the total cost per unit time of downtime losses and repair crew cost.

7.4.2 CONSTRUCTION OF MODEL

(1) The arrival rate of failed machines requiring repair is Poisson distributed with arrival rate λ.

(2) The service distribution of the repair crew is negative exponential with service rate μ.

(3) The output value per unit time for one machine working is V.

(4) The cost per unit time of the repair crew is a function of the service rate and is $c(\mu)$.

(5) The objective is to choose μ to minimize the expected costs per unit time $C(\mu)$ incurred from downtime losses and repairing the machines.

$C(\mu) =$ Output value lost due to machines waiting in a queue for repair
$+$ Output value lost while machines are being repaired by the crew
$+$ Cost of the repair crew

Output value lost due to machines waiting in queue
$=$ Value of output per uninterrupted unit of time
$\times$ Mean time one job waits in queue
$\times$ Arrival rate of jobs

$$= V\left(\frac{\rho}{\mu - \lambda}\right)\lambda$$

Note that $\rho/(\mu - \lambda)$ is the mean time that one job waits in the queue for repair (see Section 7.2.2).

> *Output value lost due to machines being repaired by crew*
> = Value of output per uninterrupted unit of time
> × Mean time one job spends being repaired
> × Arrival rate of jobs

$$= V\left(\frac{1}{\mu}\right)\lambda$$

Cost of repair crew $= c(\mu)$

Therefore

$$C(\mu) = V\left(\frac{\rho}{\mu - \lambda}\right)\lambda + V\left(\frac{1}{\mu}\right)\lambda + c(\mu)$$

$$= \frac{V\lambda}{\mu - \lambda} + c(\mu) \tag{7.2}$$

This is a model of the problem relating repair rate μ to cost.

Since we wish to minimize cost we differentiate $C(\mu)$ with respect to μ and equate to zero. This gives

$$\max c'(\mu) = \frac{V\lambda}{(\mu - \lambda)^2} \tag{7.3}$$

Since values of V, λ, μ and the form of $c(\mu)$ are known the optimal repair rate, μ, to minimize cost per unit time is that value of μ which makes the left-hand side of equation (7.3) equal to its right-hand side.

7.4.3 NUMERICAL EXAMPLE

(1) Let the arrival rate of failed machines per week $\lambda = 20$
(2) Let the output value of one machine per week $V = £10000$
(3) Assume that the repair crew cost per week is of the form

$$c(\mu) = K\mu$$

where K is a constant equal to 500 (see Figure 7.6).

Then $c'(\mu) = K$ and therefore equation (7.3) becomes:

$$\mu_{opt} = \sqrt{\left(\frac{10000 \times 20}{500}\right)} + 20 = 40 \text{ machine/week}$$

Thus the repair crew should be given sufficient incentive, say through the use of portable power tools or bonus schemes, to achieve a through-put rate of 40 machines/week.

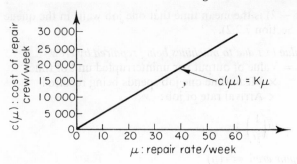

Fig. 7.6

7.4.4 FURTHER COMMENTS

Before leaving this problem it is worth noting that the idle time per week for the crew, given by the probability that there are no jobs in the queue or being served, i.e. P_0, is:

$$P_0 = 1 - \frac{\lambda}{\mu} = 1 - \frac{20}{40} = 50\%$$

and, of course, the fraction of time that the repair crew is busy per week is $50\% \ (= \lambda/\mu = \rho)$.

Figure 7.7 demonstrates that as ρ, the traffic intensity, approaches 1,

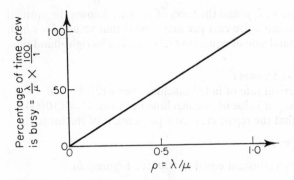

Fig. 7.7

then the proportion of time that the crew is busy approaches 100% while Figure 7.8 shows that the average time a job waits in the system rapidly approaches infinity.

Thus again we demonstrate (as in Section 7.3.3) that it may be erroneous to assume that high utilization of resources is a consequence of optimal operation of a system which calls, on occasions, for the use of these resources.

In the analysis of the above problem it has been implied that the number of potential machines that the repair crew attends to is large, otherwise the reduction in working machines when the number in the queueing system (either waiting or being repaired) is large will tend

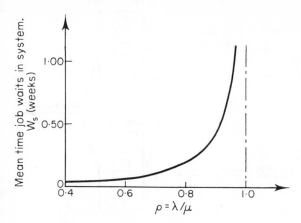

Fig. 7.8

to reduce the arrival rate of failed machines. In that case a different treatment is required (see Benson and Cox [6] and White *et al.* [49]). A related problem is covered in Section 7.6.

7.5 Optimal mix of two classes of similar equipment (such as medium/large lathes) to meet a fluctuating workload

7.5.1 STATEMENT OF PROBLEM
The problem of this section is an extension of the problem of Section 7.3 which dealt with the optimal number of identical workshop machines to meet a fluctuating demand.

Specifically, in this section we will assume that there is a class of machines, lathes used in the workshop, which can be divided into medium and large lathes. Jobs requiring lathe work can then be divided into those which require processing on a medium lathe, on a large lathe, or can be processed equally well on either. The service times of jobs on medium and large lathes differ, as do the operating costs of the lathes.

For a given workload pattern the problem is to determine the optimal mix of medium/large lathes to minimize the total cost per unit time of the lathes and downtime costs associated with jobs waiting in a queue or being processed.

7.5.2 CONSTRUCTION OF MODEL
Figure 7.9 illustrates the queueing system for the problem:

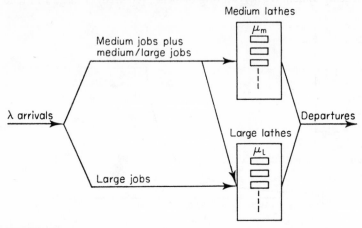

Fig. 7.9

Thus it is seen that lathe-requiring work arriving at the lathes can be divided into work which requires the use of:

    (i) a medium lathe (operating cost low);
   (ii) a large lathe (operating cost high); or
  (iii) it can be processed on either a medium or large lathe.

To attempt to analyse the above system analytically is not practicable due to the complexity of the mathematics which would be involved. Simulation is however a convenient alternative and is readily understandable. We will now introduce this procedure.

Simulation basically consists of four steps:

  (1) Determine the logic of the system being analysed and represent it by means of a flow chart.
  (2) Obtain the information necessary to work through the flow chart.
  (3) Simulate the operation of the system for different alternatives by using the data obtained in step 2 and working through the logic specified in step 1. The simulation can be done manually or by computer.
  (4) Evaluate the consequences obtained in step 3 and so identify the best alternative.

Logic flow chart

Since in practice most jobs which can be processed on a medium lathe can also be processed on a large lathe we will consider a two-queue system: one queue at the medium lathes, composed of all jobs requiring at least a medium lathe; one queue at the large lathes, composed of all jobs requiring only a large lathe.

Whenever a medium lathe becomes vacant it takes the first job in the medium/large queue and processes it. If there is no queue at the medium lathes then the medium lathes are idle.

Whenever a large lathe becomes vacant it takes the first job in the large lathes queue. If there is no queue at the large lathes then, if possible, a job is transferred from the medium/large queue to the large lathe.

The logic of the system is illustrated on the flow chart of Figure 7.10.

Obtaining necessary information and constructing model

We shall suppose that observations of the system have been made and that the following distributions have been obtained:

(a) The arrival rate of jobs to the lathe system is Poisson with arrival rate λ per unit time. Thus the inter-arrival distribution of jobs will be negative exponential with mean interval $1/\lambda$.

(b) The probability that an incoming job joins the queue at the medium lathes is p, hence the probability that the job joins the large lathe queue is $(1 - p)$.

(c) The service times for jobs on the medium and large lathes are negative exponentially distributed with mean service rates of μ_m and μ_l per unit time.

(d) The downtime cost per unit time for a job waiting in a queue or being processed is C_d.

(e) The cost of operation per unit time for one medium lathe is C_m and for one large lathe it is C_l.

The objective is to determine the optimal number of medium (n_m) and large (n_l) lathes to minimize the total cost per unit time $C(n_m, n_l)$ associated with the lathes and downtime costs of jobs being in the workshop for repair.

$C(n_m, n_l) =$ Cost per unit time for medium lathes
  $+$ Cost per unit time for large lathes
  $+$ Downtime cost per unit time for jobs waiting
  or being processed in the medium lathe system
  $+$ Downtime cost per unit time for jobs waiting
  or being processed in the large lathe system

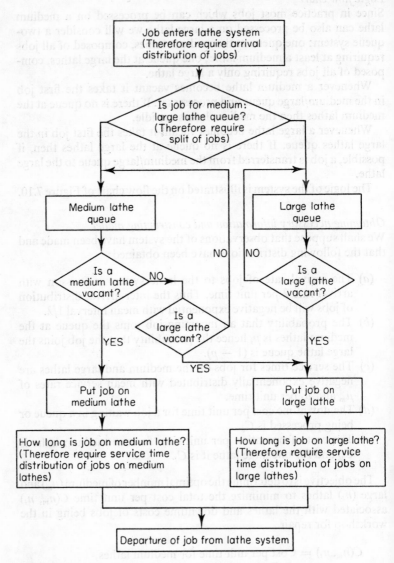

Fig. 7.10

Cost per unit time for medium lathes $= n_m C_m$
Cost per unit time for large lathes $= n_l C_l$
Downtime cost per unit time = Mean wait in system for one
for jobs waiting or being job
processed in medium system × Arrival rate of jobs to
system
× Downtime cost per unit
time per job
$= W_{s,m} \times \lambda p \times p(n_m, n_l) C_d$

[*Note*. The probability that a job enters the medium system is $p \times p(n_m, n_l)$ where $p(n_m, n_l)$ is the probability that an incoming job which is allocated to the medium/large queue is processed on a medium lathe. This "processing" probability is dependent upon the number of medium and large lathes. Then the probability that a job initially allocated to the medium/large queue is transferred to the large system is $1 - p(n_m, n_l)$.]

Similarly

Downtime cost per unit time for $= W_{s,l} \{ \lambda(1 - p)$
jobs waiting or being $+ \lambda p \left[1 - p(n_m, n_l) \right] \} C_d$
processed in large system

where $\lambda p [1 - p(n_m, n_l)]$ is the mean number of jobs which transfer from the medium/large queue to be processed on a large lathe. Therefore

$$C(n_m, n_l) = n_m C_m + n_l C_l + W_{s,m} \times \lambda p \times p(n_m, n_l) \times C_d$$
$$+ W_{s,l} \{ \lambda(1 - p) + \lambda p [1 - p(n_m, n_l)] \} C_d \quad (7.4)$$

This is a model of the problem relating mix of lathes to expected total cost. (Note that both $W_{s,m}$ and $W_{s,l}$ are functions of n_m and of n_l.)

The major problem in solving the above model is determination of the waiting times in the medium and large systems, for different mixes of lathes and the corresponding "processing" probabilities $p(n_m, n_l)$. This is obtained by simulation in the following example.

7.5.3 NUMERICAL EXAMPLE
(1) The arrival rate of jobs to the lathe section per day is Poisson distributed with mean arrival rate 10 per day. The cumulative distribution function for this is given in Figure 7.11.
(2) The probability that an incoming job joins the queue at the medium lathes is 0·8.
(3) The service distribution for jobs on a medium lathe is negative exponential with mean service rate for the lathe of 2 per day.

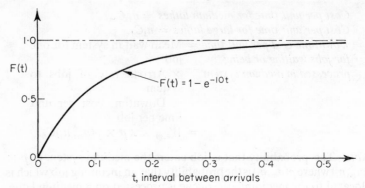

Fig. 7.11

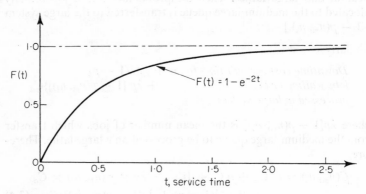

Fig. 7.12

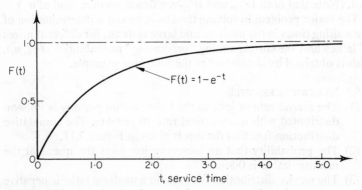

Fig. 7.13

The cumulative distribution function for this is given in Figure 7.12.

(4) The service time distribution for jobs on a large lathe is negative exponential with mean service rate for the lathe of 1 per day. The cumulative distribution function for this is given in Figure 7.13.

(5) The downtime cost per job C_d is £1 per day.

(6) The costs of operation C_m and C_l are £7 and £10 per day respectively.

(7) Determination of queueing times for jobs at the medium and large lathes is obtained by simulation as follows.

Firstly, we must assume a certain number of medium and large lathes. We might estimate this as follows.

There are 10 jobs per day, on average, arriving at the lathes. 80% require a medium lathe. Therefore

8 jobs per day require a medium lathe, and

2 jobs per day require a large lathe.

A medium lathe can process, on average, 2 jobs per day.

A large lathe can process, on average, 1 job per day.

Let us assume that we have 4 medium lathes and 3 large lathes.

Note. If we only had 2 large lathes, which might appear to be sufficient, then the traffic intensity of the system ρ would be 1. As we have seen (sample calculation of Section 7.3.3) this would lead to infinite waiting times.

With reference to the logic flow chart (Figure 7.10):

(1) Assume job 1 arrives at lathe at time 0.

(2) Select a number between 00 and 99 from a table of random sampling numbers (see Table 7.2 for extract). If it is < 80 then job goes to medium queue, otherwise it goes to large queue. Taking the first 2-digit number on Table 7.2 we get "20", therefore job 1 goes to the medium lathes.

(3) Select another number from Table 7.2. This number is now used to determine the duration of job 1 on a medium lathe. The next 2-digit number in row 1 is 17. This is taken as 0·17 and is marked on the y-axis of Figure 7.12. Drawing a horizontal line from 0·17 till it cuts the $F(t)$ curve, then dropping a vertical line, gives a service time of 0·10 days as being equivalent to a random number of "17".

Note. In this example the random sampling numbers are taken to be in the range 0·005 to 0·995 in steps of 0·01 to preclude the possibility of a zero or infinite service time being specified.

Table 7.2

20 17	42 28	23 17	59 66	38 61	02 10	86 10	51 55	92 52	44 25
74 49	04 49	03 04	10 33	53 70	11 54	48 63	94 60	94 49	57 38
94 70	49 31	38 67	23 42	29 65	40 88	78 71	37 18	48 64	06 57
22 15	78 15	69 84	32 52	32 54	15 12	54 02	01 37	38 37	12 93
93 29	12 18	27 30	30 55	91 87	50 57	58 51	49 36	12 53	96 40
45 04	77 97	36 14	99 45	52 95	69 85	03 83	51 87	85 56	22 37
44 91	99 49	89 39	94 60	48 49	06 77	64 72	59 26	08 51	25 57
16 23	91 02	19 96	47 59	89 65	27 84	30 92	63 37	26 24	23 66
04 50	65 04	65 65	82 42	70 51	55 04	61 47	88 83	99 34	82 37
32 70	17 72	03 61	66 26	24 71	22 77	88 33	17 78	08 92	73 49

Extract of random sampling numbers taken from Lindley and Miller.*
Each digit is an independent sample from a population in which the
digits 0 to 9 are equally likely, that is each has a probability of 1/10.

Thus a random number of 17 is equivalent to $F(t) = 0.175$. So
$0.175 = 1 - e^{-2t}$, and therefore $t = 0.10$ days.

(4) As there are no other jobs in the system we can put job 1 straight
on to a medium lathe, say m_1, the first medium lathe, for 0.1
days.

All the above information is given in the first row of Table 7.3.

(5) We now have to generate the arrival of another job. To do this
we select a further random number, in this case "42" from the
top row of Table 7.2. Marking 0.42 on the y-axis of Figure 7.12
we get an equivalent interval between job 1 and job 2 of 0.06
day from the x-axis.

Proceeding as indicated for 2, 3 and 4 above the second row of
Table 7.3 can be completed. The interval between arrival of job 2 and
job 3 can be obtained as indicated for 5 above and the row 3 of Table
7.3 can be completed as per 2, 3 and 4 above. Similarly, rows 4, 5, 6 and
7 of the Table can be completed.

Clearly the construction of a table such as Table 7.3 by hand is
tedious. However if we proceeded as above we would eventually
generate sufficient jobs to obtain the average waiting time (from
columns 6 and 7) for jobs in the medium or large lathe systems when
there are 4 medium and 3 large lathes and the probability $p(4, 3)$ of
jobs being processed on the medium lathes (from columns 4 and 5).
To reduce the tediousness and speed up the calculations it is usually
possible to take advantage of one of the many computer languages
which are available to perform the simulation. Using such a language
Table 7.4(a) is obtained which gives the mean waiting time results for

* Lindley, D. V. and Miller, J. C. P., *Cambridge Elementary Statistical
Tables*, Cambridge University Press, 1964 (p. 12).

Table 7.3

1	2	3	4	5	6	7	8	9	10	11
Job no.	Inter-arrival time be-tween jobs	Cumu-lative time	Queue decision	Is a suit-able lathe vacant?	Waiting time in queue	Service time on lathe (days)	Lathe used	Starting time on lathe	Finishing time on lathe (cumu-lative time)	Next job on lathe
1		0:00	r.n. = 20 m queue	Yes	0	r.n. = 17 0:10	m_1	0:00	0:10	6
2	r.n. = 42 0:06	0:06	r.n. = 28 m queue	Yes	0	r.n. = 23 0:13	m_2	0:06	0:06 + 0:13 0:19	7
3	r.n. = 17 0:02	0:08	r.n. = 59 m queue	Yes	0	r.n. = 66 0:55	m_3	0:08	0:08 + 0:55 0:63	
4	r.n. = 38 0:05	0:13	r.n. = 61 m queue	Yes	0	r.n. = 2 0:01	m_4	0:13	0:13 + 0:01 0:14	
5	r.n. = 10 0:01	0:14	r.n. = 86 l queue	Yes	0	r.n. = 10 0:11	l_1	0:14	0:14 + 0:11 0:25	
6	r.n. = 51 0:07	0:21	r.n. = 55 m queue	Yes (m_1 is vacant at time 0:10)	0	r.n. = 92 1:30	m_1	0:21	0:21 + 1:30 1:51	
7	r.n. = 52 0:07	0:28	r.n. = 44 m queue	Yes (m_2 is vacant at time 0:19)	0	r.n. = 25 0:15	m_2	0:28	0:28 + 0:15 0:43	

the data used in construction of Table 7.3 and the "processing" probability $p(4, 3)$.

Table 7.4(a)

$n_m = 4$	$W_{s,m} = 4 \cdot 23$	$p(4, 3) = 0 \cdot 91$
$n_l = 3$	$W_{s,l} = 7 \cdot 86$	

Table 7.4(b)

$n_m = 5$	$W_{s,m} = 3 \cdot 08$	$p(5, 3) = 0 \cdot 93$
$n_l = 3$	$W_{s\,l} = 6 \cdot 13$	
$n_m = 6$	$W_{s,m} = 2 \cdot 60$	$p(6, 3) = 0 \cdot 94$
$n_l = 3$	$W_{s,l} = 5 \cdot 75$	
$n_m = 4$	$W_{s,m} = 3 \cdot 60$	$p(4, 4) = 0 \cdot 82$
$n_l = 4$	$W_{s,l} = 4 \cdot 92$	
$n_m = 5$	$W_{s,m} = 2 \cdot 51$	$p(5, 4) = 0 \cdot 87$
$n_l = 4$	$W_{s,l} = 4 \cdot 43$	
$n_m = 6$	$W_{s,m} = 2 \cdot 49$	$p(6, 4) = 0 \cdot 92$
$n_l = 4$	$W_{s,l} = 4 \cdot 29$	

Table 7.4(*b*) gives the appropriate mean waiting times and "processing" probabilities for other feasible combinations of numbers of medium and large lathes, i.e. ones which result in a steady state.

Once the waiting times and probabilities have been determined then solutions can be obtained to the model, equation (7.4). Table 7.5 gives the various total costs per day and it is seen that the optimal mix is 5 medium and 3 large lathes.

Sample Calculation

When $n_m = 4$, $n_l = 3$, $p = 0 \cdot 8$, $\lambda = 10$, then from the simulation we obtain $W_{s,m} = 4 \cdot 23$ days, $W_{s,l} = 7 \cdot 86$ days. These are the mean times which jobs processed on medium and large lathes spent in the system.

Table 7.5

(n_m, n_l)	$C(n_m, n_l)$
$n_m = 4$ $n_l = 3$	110·26
$n_m = 5$ $n_l = 3$	103·66
$n_m = 6$ $n_l = 3$	105·66
$n_m = 4$ $n_l = 4$	108·46
$n_m = 5$ $n_l = 4$	105·72
$n_m = 6$ $n_l = 4$	111·61

The probability that a job which is allocated to the medium/large queue on entry to the system is processed on a medium lathe, $p(4, 3)$, is obtained as 0·91. Therefore the probability that a job is switched from the medium/large queue to be processed on a large lathe is $1 - 0·91 = 0·09$. We therefore obtain

$$C(4, 3) = 4 \times 7 + 3 \times 10 + 4 \times 23(10 \times 0·8 \times 0·91) \times 1$$
$$+ 7·86(10 \times 0·2 + 10 \times 0·8 \times 0·09) \times 1$$
$$= £110·26 \text{ per day}$$

Note. For each combination of medium and large lathes 4 simulation runs were made on the computer to obtain the waiting time statistics. Each run, which was equivalent to 2 months operation took $\frac{1}{4}$ hour.

7.5.4 FURTHER COMMENTS

Simulation is a very useful procedure for tackling complex (and not so complex) queueing type problems. The reader interested in a fairly complete discussion of the subject is referred to Tocher [10] or Naylor *et al.* [36].

In the model it was assumed that the processing time for a job which could be done on a medium lathe, but which was switched to a large lathe, could be taken from the same service time distribution as a job requiring processing on a large lathe. This may be realistic, since medium jobs may require longer setting up times on a large lathe and thus offset the increased speed of doing the job on the larger lathe. However, if this assumption is not acceptable then the model would need to be modified. Also in the model it was implied that the operating cost of a lathe was constant and independent of whether or not the lathe was being used. Removal of these assumptions is not difficult but a more complicated model would result than the one discussed in this section.

It will be appreciated that in construction of Table 7.5 the appropriate mixes of medium and large lathes to use in the simulation were obtained on a subjective basis—through careful thought about the consequences resulting from previously tried combinations. Thus it is obvious that the use of simulation may result in the optimum being missed since it is often not feasible to attempt to evaluate all possible alternatives. In practice this is not usually a severe restriction.

Another problem with simulation is to decide just how many "runs" should be made since it is only after a sufficiently large number of runs are made that the "steady state" is reached and averages can be calculated and used in a model. Discussion of the "cut-off" point, and other aspects of experimental design, is covered in the two textbooks referred to at the beginning of this section.

For "simple" problems a hand simulation may be worthwhile and if this is done tables of random numbers will be required. Table 7.2 was an extract of such tables which appear in many books of statistical tables. Tables of random numbers consist of a sequence of the digits 0, 1, . . ., 9, having the property that any position in the sequence has an equal probability of containing any one of these 10 digits. Such sequences can be broken down into subsequences of n-digits having the same property. Suppose it is necessary to draw an item at random from a population of 1 000 items. If these items are imagined to carry labels with numbers ranging from 000 to 999 selecting an item at random is then equivalent to selecting a 3-digit number at random. This condition is satisfied by entering the table at any point and selecting the item corresponding to that number in the table. Repetition of this process allows a random sample of any desired size to be selected provided that the 3-digit numbers taken from the table are accepted every time in the same sequence.

Conversion of random sampling numbers to random variables (as is done in the simulation example of Section 7.5.3) is done via the appropriate cumulative distribution function of the variable. Once a random sampling number is obtained (from tables) the corresponding value of the random variable is read off the distribution function (see Section 7.5.3). In the example 2-digit random sampling numbers were used (in range 00 to 99) and then taken to be in the range 0·005 to 0·995 in steps of 0·01.

Although the example of this section dealt specifically with determination of the optimal mix of lathes in a workshop the approach is applicable to other maintenance problems. For example, a problem that frequently occurs is the necessity to determine the appropriate skills to have available in a maintenance team and the number of men possessing these skills. Certain jobs can be tackled equally well by any member of the team, while others require specialists. The different classes of skills which can be defined will almost certainly exceed two but even so the optimal mix of these skills can be determined in a manner similar to that of this section.

Finally, in the model it has been assumed that downtime cost could be obtained. As is often the case this is a difficult costing problem and so the analysis of such a problem may stop at determination of the consequences in terms of waiting times for different mixes of lathes, with management then deciding which alternative they prefer on the basis of the calculated waiting times.

7.6 Optimal number of machines/repair crew: the machine interference problem

7.6.1 STATEMENT OF PROBLEM

A repair crew is responsible for looking after n machines and repairing them when they break down. Thus there is a finite maximum number of possible jobs n, requiring attention by the repair crew at any time. The arrival rate of incoming jobs (failed machines) to the repair crew will then depend, in part, on the number of machines n allocated to the repair crew and how many of these machines r are waiting for repair or being repaired. (In the examples of Sections 7.3–7.5 it was assumed that the arrival rate remained constant.) It is assumed that only one machine can be repaired by the repair crew at any time.

The basic conflicts of the problem are that as n increases the repair crew will be busier and so the cost of repairs per machine will decrease, but there will be an increase in downtime losses incurred because failed machines have to wait longer in a queue before they can be repaired. Machine interference is the term used to describe the problem since incoming machine breakdowns may have to wait until the repair crew is free from attending to earlier breakdowns, i.e. the repair of one machine may interfere with the immediate repair of subsequent machines. The problem is to determine the optimal allocation of machines to a repair crew to minimize the total cost of repairs and downtime losses per machine per unit time.

7.6.2 CONSTRUCTION OF MODEL

(1) The failure distribution of a machine is negative exponential with mean time to failure $1/\lambda$, i.e. the arrival rate is λ per unit of machine operating time.

(2) The time required to repair a failed machine is negative exponentially distributed with mean repair time $1/\mu$.

(3) Given λ and μ, the mean time required by a repair crew to keep one machine operating for a unit time is $\lambda/\mu = \rho$, say. This is illustrated in Figure 7.14 where, if one unit of machine

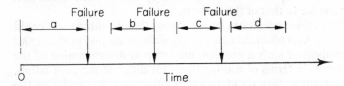

Fig. 7.14

operating time is $a + b + c + d$, the time spent by the repair crew to obtain this unit of time is: Mean number of failures per unit of machine operating time × Mean repair time per repair $= \lambda \times 1/\mu$.

(4) Following from (3), if one unit of machine operating time requires ρ units of time being repaired, then one unit of time in repair results in $1/\rho$ units of machine operating time.

(5) The profit value of machine output per unit of machine operating time is P (i.e. if no downtime losses occur).

(6) The fixed cost of the repair crew per unit time is R.

(7) The objective is to determine the optimal number of machines n to allocate to a repair crew to minimize the total costs per machine of repairs and downtime per unit time. Letting $C(n)$ be this total,

$C(n)$ = Repair cost per machine per unit time
  + Downtime losses per machine per unit time
Repair cost per machine per unit time $= R/n$
Downtime losses per machine per unit time
  $= (1 - \text{Availability of 1 machine per unit time}) \times P$

Now, utilization of repair crew is U_c for n machines, therefore the mean time the crew spends repairing 1 machine per unit time is U_c/n. From (4), 1 unit of repair time results from $1/\rho$ units of machine operating time, therefore U_c/n units of repair time result from

$U_c/n\rho$ units of operating time, which is the availability per unit time of one machine. Therefore

$$C(n) = \frac{R}{n} + \left(1 - \frac{U_c}{n\rho}\right) \times P \qquad (7.5)$$

This is a model of the problem relating machine allocation per repair crew, n, to total cost $C(n)$ per machine per unit time. Before proceeding with a numerical example it is necessary to make a few comments about determination of repair crew utilization.

Repair crew utilization U_c

As indicated in the Statement of Problem the arrival rate of jobs to the repair crew at any time depends on the number of machines n allocated to the crew, and the number of these r either waiting for repair or being repaired. The crew utilization is the proportion of time that at least one of the n machines is in a failed state and this is a function of both ρ and n. For given values of ρ and n Cox and Smith [13] give the appropriate equations to determine U_c. For values of n up to 14, Table 7.6, which is taken from Cox and Smith, can be used to determine U_c. Interpolation for specific values of ρ or n may be necessary.

7.6.3 NUMERICAL EXAMPLE

(1) Letting the mean time to failure of a machine $1/\lambda = 2.5$ weeks, the mean repair time for one machine $1/\mu = \frac{1}{2}$ week, then $\rho = \lambda/\mu = 0.2$.
(2) Letting the profit value per uninterrupted week P (i.e. if no downtime losses occur) be £500, the repair crew cost per week R is £800, from equation (7.5),

$$C(n) = \frac{800}{n} + \left(1 - \frac{U_c}{n \times 0.2}\right) \times 500$$

Solution of the above equation for different values of n is given in Table 7.7, which indicates that the optimal allocation of machines to a repair crew is 6.

Sample calculation

When $n = 2$ and $\rho = 0.2$, from Table 7.6 the repair crew utilization is 0.324. Thus equation (7.5) becomes

$$C(2) = \frac{800}{2} + \left(1 - \frac{0.324}{2 \times 0.2}\right) 500 = £495$$

Table 7.6 Repair crew utilization with n machines/repair crew

n \ ρ	0·8	0·7	0·6	0·4	0·2
1	0·444	0·412	0·375	0·286	0·167
2	0·742	0·704	0·658	0·528	0·324
3	0·903	0·876	0·840	0·718	0·470
4	0·971	0·958	0·938	0·850	0·602
6	0·998	0·997	0·994	0·972	0·808
8	1·000	1·000	1·000	0·997	0·930
10				1·000	0·982
12					0·997

n \ ρ	0·18	0·16	0·14	0·12	0·10
2	0·298	0·271	0·242	0·212	0·180
4	0·560	0·515	0·465	0·412	0·353
6	0·767	0·718	0·660	0·592	0·516
8	0·902	0·864	0·813	0·746	0·662
10	0·969	0·949	0·916	0·863	0·785
12	0·993	0·986	0·970	0·939	0·880
14	0·999	0·997	0·992	0·978	0·943

Table 7.7

n	1	2	3	4	5	6	7	8
$C(n)$	882	495	375	323	307	296	309	310

7.6.4 FURTHER COMMENTS

One important assumption in the machine interference model was that the repair crew was always available so that, whenever a breakdown occurred, and there were no previously failed machines in a queue or being repaired, then repair could be started immediately. There is, however, the possibility that when the crew is idle it attends to "fill-up" work. If this is the case there may be delays incurred between a machine failure occurring and the repair crew starting repair. Also if "fill-up" work is done then part of the cost of the repair crew should be allocated to that work. Some discussion of complications arising from the occurrence of "fill-up" work is given by Cox and Smith [13].

7.7 Optimal size of a maintenance work force to meet a fluctuating workload, taking account of subcontracting opportunities

7.7.1 STATEMENT OF PROBLEM

The workload for the maintenance crew is specified at the beginning of a period, say a week. By the end of the week all the workload must be completed. The size of the work force is fixed, thus there is a fixed number of manhours available per week. If demand at the beginning of the week requires fewer manhours than the fixed capacity then no subcontracting takes place. If, however, the demand is greater than the capacity then the excess workload is subcontracted and returned from the subcontractor by the end of the week.

Two sorts of costs are incurred:

(a) Fixed cost depending on the size of the work force.
(b) Variable cost depending on the mix of internal/external workload.

As the fixed cost is increased through increasing the size of the work force then there is less chance of subcontracting being necessary. However, there may frequently be occasions when fixed costs will be incurred yet demand may be low, i.e. considerable under-utilization of work force. The problem is to determine the optimal size of the work force to meet a fluctuating demand to minimize expected total cost per unit time.

7.7.2 CONSTRUCTION OF MODEL

(1) The demand per unit time is distributed according to a probability density function $f(r)$, where r is the number of jobs.
(2) The average number of jobs processed per man per unit time is m.
(3) The total capacity of the work force per unit time is mn, where n is the number of men in the work force.
(4) The average cost of processing one job by the work force is C_w.
(5) The average cost of processing one job by the subcontractor is C_s.
(6) The fixed cost per man per unit time is C_f.

The basic conflicts of this problem are illustrated in Figure 7.15 from which it is seen that the expected total cost per unit time $C(n)$ is

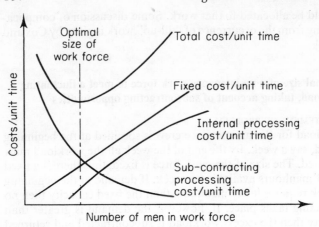

Fig. 7.15

$C(n)$ = Fixed cost per unit time
+ Variable internal processing cost per unit time
+ Variable subcontracting processing cost per unit time.

Fixed cost per unit time = Size of work force
× Fixed cost per man
= nC_f

Variable internal processing = Average number of jobs
cost per unit time   processed internally per unit time
× Cost per job

Now, number of jobs processed internally per unit time will be

(i) equal to the capacity when demand is greater than capacity;
(ii) equal to demand when demand is less than, or equal to, capacity.

Probability of (i) = $\int_{nm}^{\infty} f(r) \, dr$

Probability of (ii) = $\int_{0}^{nm} f(r) \, dr = 1 - \int_{nm}^{\infty} f(r) \, dr$

When (ii) occurs, the average demand will be

$$\int_{0}^{nm} rf(r) \, dr \Big/ \int_{0}^{nm} f(r) \, dr$$

Therefore *variable internal processing cost per unit time* is

$$\left(nm \int_{nm}^{\infty} f(r)\, dr + \frac{\int_{0}^{nm} rf(r)\, dr}{\int_{0}^{nm} f(r)\, dr} \int_{0}^{nm} f(r)\, dr \right) C_w$$

Variable subcontracting = Average number of jobs
processing cost per unit time processed externally per unit
time
× Cost per job

Now, number of jobs processed externally will be

(i) zero when the demand is less that the work force capacity;
(ii) equal to the difference between demand and capacity when demand is greater than capacity.

Probability of (i) $= \int_{0}^{nm} f(r)\, dr$

Probability of (ii) $= \int_{nm}^{\infty} f(r)\, dr = 1 - \int_{0}^{nm} f(r)\, dr$

When (ii) occurs the average number of jobs subcontracted is:

$$\int_{nm}^{\infty} (r - nm) f(r)\, dr \Big/ \int_{nm}^{\infty} f(r)\, dr$$

Therefore *variable subcontracting processing cost per unit time* is

$$\left(0 \times \int_{0}^{nm} f(r)\, dr + \frac{\int_{nm}^{\infty} (r - nm)f(r)\, dr}{\int_{nm}^{\infty} f(r)\, dr} \int_{nm}^{\infty} f(r)\, dr \right) C_s$$

Therefore

$$C(n) = nC_f + \left(nm \int_{nm}^{\infty} f(r)\, dr + \int_{0}^{nm} rf(r)\, dr \right) C_w$$

$$+ \left(\int_{nm}^{\infty} (r - nm)\, f(r)\, dr \right) C_s \qquad (7.6)$$

This is a model of the problem relating work force size n to total cost per unit time $C(n)$.

7.7.3 NUMERICAL EXAMPLE

(1) It is assumed that the demand distribution of jobs per week can be represented by a rectangular distribution having range $(30, 70)$, i.e. $f(r) = 1/40$, $30 \leqslant r \leqslant 70$, $f(r) = 0$ elsewhere.

(2) $m = 10$ jobs per week, $C_w = £2$, $C_s = £10$, $C_f = £40$.

Equation (7.6) becomes

$$C(n) = n40 + \left(n10 \int_{10n}^{70} \frac{1}{40} \, dr + \int_{30}^{10n} r \frac{1}{40} \, dr \right) 2 \\ + \left(\int_{10n}^{70} (r - 10n) \frac{1}{40} \, dr \right) 10$$

Table 7.8, which gives the values of $C(n)$ for all possible values of n, indicates that for the costs used in the example, the optimal solution is to have a work force of five men.

Table 7.8

n	0	1	2	3	4	5	6	7
$C(n)$	500	460	420	380	350	340	352	380

Sample calculation
When $n = 5$,

$$C(n) = 200 + \left(50 \int_{50}^{70} \frac{1}{40} \, dr + \int_{30}^{50} r \frac{1}{40} \, dr \right) 2 \\ + \left(\int_{50}^{70} (r - 50) \frac{1}{40} \, dr \right) 10 \\ = 200 + (50 \times 0{\cdot}5 + 20)2 + 5 \times 10 = £340$$

7.7.4 FURTHER COMMENTS

In construction of the model of this section it was assumed that all jobs requiring attention at the start of a week had to be completed by the end of the week. In practice this requirement would not be necessary if jobs could be "carried-over" from one week to another. Inclusion of this condition would result in a model more complicated than that of equation (7.6).

8 Reliability Decisions

8.1 Introduction

The way in which the build-up of equipment within a system or components within an equipment occurs influences the reliability of the system or of the equipment. Thus when examining equipment configuration two aspects need to be considered:

(*a*) The interdependence of equipment within a group.
(*b*) The physical structure of a single equipment.

THE INTERDEPENDENCE OF EQUIPMENT

Equipment (such as machines) within a system (such as a production system) is interdependent because each depends on the successful operation of the others before it too can "produce" and result in total operation of the system. For example, in a series configuration such as Figure 8.1 the workpiece passes through machines *A*, *B*, *C* and *D*. If

Fig. 8.1

any of these machines is inoperative there is a potential source of production loss. To reduce this potential loss machines can be put in parallel with "critical" machines, such as illustrated in the series/parallel configuration of Figure 8.2. Thus if machine *C* is the critical machine then putting two machines in parallel, one of which acts as a standby, reduces the possibility of production losses occurring.

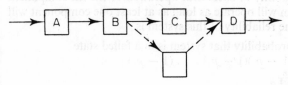

Fig. 8.2

THE PHYSICAL STRUCTURE OF A SINGLE EQUIPMENT

A single equipment in general will itself be composed of several subsystems, which may be interdependent in both a series and parallel form as illustrated above.

Alternative equipment configurations may result in different costs, reliabilities, space requirements, safety levels, etc., and in this chapter we will examine several problems associated with identifying optimal equipment configurations taking into account reliability considerations.

Before examining such problems we will first introduce possible design configurations of systems or equipments and show how the probability of successful operation of these designs can be calculated. The reliability of any configuration is the probability that the configuration will operate in the manner envisaged in the design.

8.2 Some basic probability considerations

(a) *Series configuration* (Figure 8.3)

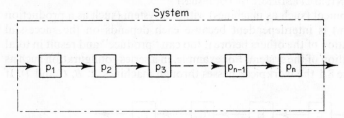

Fig. 8.3

If p_i is the probability of successful operation of component i then the probability that the system will operate successfully, i.e. the reliability of the system, R_s, is

$$R_s = p_1 \times p_2 \times p_3 \times \ldots \times p_n = \prod_{i=1}^{n} p_i$$

(b) *Parallel configuration* (Figure 8.4)

If p_i is the probability of successful operation of the ith component and, if the system will operate as long as at least one component will function, then the reliability of this system is

$$R_s = 1 - \text{probability that system is in a failed state}$$
$$= 1 - (1 - p_1)(1 - p_2) \ldots (1 - p_n)$$
$$= 1 - \prod_{i=1}^{n} q_i$$

System

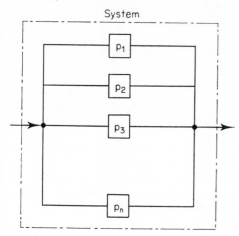

Fig. 8.4

where $q_i = 1 - p_i$ is the probability of failure (i.e. unsuccessful operation) of the ith component.

Note that the above configuration is termed parallel redundancy. It is assumed that only one component operates at any time and it continues operating until it fails, when the system switches to using the next component in parallel which is used until it fails, and so on until all n components have failed. Only then will the system not perform its required function. The above reliability calculation also assumes that once a component fails it remains failed and is not repaired and returned to the system. (The opportunity of making repairs will be included in the example of Section 8.7.)

(*c*) *Combined series/parallel configuration* (Figure 8.5)
The reliability of the system is the probability that at least one component will function when required in each stage. Thus:

$$R_s = \prod_{i=1}^{k} (1 - q_i^{n_i})$$

when components within a stage are identical.

(*d*) *System/Component redundancy*
For a series system such as that illustrated in (*a*) the reliability of the system is

$$R_s = \prod_{i=1}^{n} p_i$$

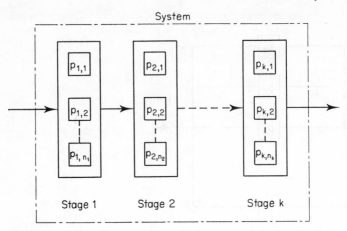

Fig. 8.5 System composed of k stages in series, with n_i components in the ith stage.

To increase the reliability of such a system two such series systems could be put in parallel (Figure 8.6).

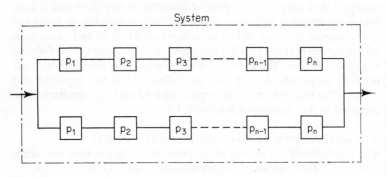

Fig. 8.6

If one system fails, the second series system takes over. In that case the reliability of such a total system is obtained as follows.

Since the reliability of one series system is defined as $\prod_{i=1}^{n} p_i$ then

Probability of failure of the system is $\left(1 - \prod_{i=1}^{n} p_i\right)$.

The reliability of the two series system in parallel is then the probability that at least one will operate, which equals 1 — probability that both will fail. Thus

$$R_s = 1 - \left(1 - \prod_{i=1}^{n} p_i\right)^2$$

An alternative to increasing the reliability of the single series system by putting two such systems in parallel is the increase in redundancy at the component level by duplicating each component, as illustrated in Figure 8.7.

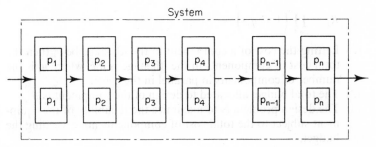

Fig. 8.7

The reliability of the above system is then, from (*c*),

$$R_s = \prod_{i=1}^{n} (1 - q_i^2)$$

(e) *Active redundancy*

In the above configurations it was assumed that when components were in parallel only one was used at any one time. Thus other parallel components were in standby. If a system operates with all parallel components operating when possible, but where failure of a component does not create system failure since the system can operate with less than the full complement of components (e.g., aircraft engines), we are dealing with active redundancy, rather than standby redundancy. Such a problem will be covered in Section 8.7. References are made later to problems concerning more complex equipment configurations.

8.3 Optimal design configuration of a series/parallel system: maximizing reliability subject to a budgetary constraint

8.3.1 STATEMENT OF PROBLEM

Equipment is composed of *k* stages in series and is only operable if each stage is in a functioning state. To increase the reliability of the equipment, components can be reproduced, in parallel, in each stage. Such a procedure is termed standby redundancy since only one component is required to operate in a stage. Given the failure probabilities of various components the problem is to determine the optimal design configuration of the equipment to maximize its reliability subject to a budgetary constraint.

8.3.2 CONSTRUCTION OF MODEL

(1) The equipment configuration we are considering is illustrated in (c) of Section 8.2. The reliability of such a system is

$$R_s = \prod_{i=1}^{k} \left(1 - q_i^{n_i} \right)$$

(2) Letting the cost of a component in the ith stage be c_i then the total cost of components in the ith stage is $n_i c_i$ where n_i is the number of components in parallel in the stage.

(3) The total budget allocated to design of the equipment is B.

(4) The design problem is to maximize the reliability of the equipment subject to the total cost of components not exceeding the budget.

Thus the problem is

$$\text{maximize} \prod_{i=1}^{k} (1 - q_i^{n_i}) \tag{8.1}$$

subject to $\sum_{i=1}^{k} n_i c_i \leqslant B$.

This is a model of the problem relating component numbers n_i to equipment reliability and cost.

8.3.3 NUMERICAL EXAMPLE

Equipment is composed of three stages. Components can be reproduced in parallel in the first two stages. There can only be one component in the third stage.

The probabilities that, at any time, a component is in a functioning state in stages 1, 2 and 3 are $p_1 = 0.9, p_2 = 0.7, p_3 = 0.9$. Therefore the respective probabilities of a component being in a failed state are: $q_1 = 0.1, q_2 = 0.3, q_3 = 0.1$.

The component costs are $c_1 = £2000, c_2 = £3000, c_3 = £1000$. The total budget $B = £10000$.

From the model

$$\text{Maximize } (1 - q_1^{n_1})(1 - q_2^{n_2})(1 - q_3^{n_3})$$
$$= (1 - 0.1^{n_1})(1 - 0.3^{n_2})(1 - 0.1)$$

subject to: $n_1c_1 + n_2c_2 + n_3c_3 \leqslant B$

$$= n_1 2000 + n_2 3000 + 1000 \leqslant 10000$$

Since the third stage is fixed, with one component costing £1000 the above conditions are equivalent to

Maximize $(1 - 0.1^{n_1})(1 - 0.3^{n_2})$

subject to $2000n_1 + 3000n_2 \leqslant 9000$.

The optimal values of n_1 and n_2, can be obtained by trial and error as follows. If $n_1 = 1$, then

$$2000 + 3000n_2 \leqslant 9000 \qquad \text{i.e. } n_2 \leqslant 2.33$$

Therefore let $n_2 = 2$.

If $n_1 = 1$, $n_2 = 2$, $R_s = (1 - 0.1^1)(1 - 0.3^2)(1 - 0.1) = 0.737$
If $n_1 = 2$, then $4000 + 3000n_2 \leqslant 9000 \qquad \text{i.e. } n_2 \leqslant 1.66$

Therefore let $n_2 = 1$.

If $n_1 = 2$, $n_2 = 1$, $R_s = (1 - 0.1^2)(1 - 0.3^1)(1 - 0.1) = 0.624$
If $n_1 = 3$, then $6000 + 3000n_2 \leqslant 9000 \qquad \text{i.e. } n_2 \leqslant 1$

Therefore let $n_2 = 1$.

If $n_1 = 3$, $n_2 = 1$, $R_s = (1 - 0.1^3)(1 - 0.3^1)(1 - 0.1) = 0.629$

Any other combination of (n_1, n_2) will result in the budgetary constraint being exceeded.

Thus the maximum reliability of the equipment occurs with 1 component in the first stage and 2 components in the second stage. The overall reliability of the three stages is 0.737 and the associated total cost is $2000 + 2(3000) + 1000 = £9000$.

8.3.4 FURTHER COMMENTS

When considering the possible benefits to be derived from redundancy of highly reliable components it should be noted that often very little is obtained for the extra cost of redundancy. This is demonstrated in the above example when three components are placed in the first stage, rather than two, and yet the reliability of the system is increased only by 0.005 for an extra £1000 in equipment cost.

Also in the example of this section there was a budgetary constraint placed on the possible design configuration of the equipment. In some problems the constraint on duplication of components (which can be thought of as allocation of redundancy) may result from their weight or space requirements. There is also the possibility that increasing the number of components in parallel at a particular stage may result in increasing the chance of the equipment operating prematurely. Such a problem will be discussed in Section 8.4.

The solution method adopted for the numerical example above is adequate for simple problems. For more complex problems relating to series/parallel systems dynamic programming can be used. The use of dynamic programming to solve the problem posed in this section is illustrated by Bellman and Dreyfus [5], who also give an example of its use where there are two constraints, cost and weight, on the design configuration. A further procedure, the Lagrange multiplier method, which could be used to solve the model is given by Rau [39].

8.4 Optimal design configuration of a series/parallel system: maximizing reliability subject to constraints on safety and budget levels

8.4.1 STATEMENT OF PROBLEM

Increasing the complexity of equipment design through the use of redundancy, thus increasing the reliability of the equipment, may also result in increasing the probability of premature operation of the equipment. This would be the case for instance in electronic equipment if no controlled input signal to the equipment is made, but a spurious signal is picked up which triggers off operation of a component of the system which, once triggered off, then sets into operation the other stages of the equipment. Conversely, increasing the safety of such equipment may result in decreasing its reliability.

The problem examined in this section is to determine the optimal design configuration of equipment composed of k stages, with n_i components in parallel in the ith stage, and where each stage must function to result in equipment operation, to maximize its reliability subject to: (a) a safety constraint in terms of the probability of premature operation of the equipment; and (b) a budgetary constraint.

8.4.2 CONSTRUCTION OF MODEL

(1) The equipment configuration we are considering is illustrated in (c) of Section 8.2. The reliability of such a configuration is

$$R_s = \prod_{i=1}^{k} (1 - q_i^{n_i})$$

(2) It is assumed that premature operation of the equipment would occur if a component in the first stage operated as a result of picking up a spurious signal, and this component then triggers off the remaining stages. The probability of a component in the first stage operating in the absence of a controlled input signal is P.

(3) The probability of the equipment operating when there is no controlled input signal is:

> Probability 1st stage operates
> × Probability 2nd stage operates . . . .
> × Probability kth stage operates

Now, probability of a component in the first stage picking up a spurious signal is P. Therefore the probability of a component not picking up the signal is $Q = 1 - P$. Therefore

> Probability of 1st stage not functioning due to a spurious signal $= Q^{n_1}$
> Probability of 1st stage operating due to a spurious signal $= (1 - Q^{n_1})$
> Probability of equipment operating where there is no controlled input signal $= (1 - Q^{n_1}) \prod_{i=2}^{k} (1 - q_i^{n_i})$

(4) The safety constraint on the design configuration is that the probability of premature operation of the equipment due to a signal must be less than or equal to S. Thus

$$(1 - Q^{n_1}) \prod_{i=2}^{k} (1 - q_i^{n_i}) \leqslant S$$

(5) The budgetary constraint on the design configuration is

$$\sum_{i=1}^{k} n_i c_i \leqslant B$$

where $n_i c_i$ is the total cost of components in the ith stage and B is the budget allocated to the design of the equipment.

The problem is then to determine the optimal number of components in parallel in each stage of the equipment to

$$\text{Maximize } \prod_{i=1}^{k} (1 - q_i^{n_i}) \qquad \text{equipment reliability}$$

$$\text{subject to } (1 - Q^{n_1}) \prod_{i=2}^{k} (1 - q_i^{n_i}) \leqslant S \qquad \text{safety constraint}$$

$$\text{and } \sum_{i=1}^{k} n_i c_i \leqslant B \qquad \text{budgetary constraint} \qquad (8.2)$$

This is a model of the problem relating component numbers n_i to equipment reliability, safety and cost.

8.4.3 NUMERICAL EXAMPLE
Using the same data as used in the previous numerical example (Section 8.3.3), namely: $k = 3$, $q_1 = 0.1$, $q_2 = 0.3$, $q_3 = 0.1$, c_1

$= £2000$, $c_2 = £3000$, $c_3 = £1000$, $B = £10000$; and letting the safety constraint $S = 0.075$, and the probability of a component in the 1st stage not responding to a spurious input signal $Q = 0.95$ we evaluate the model as follows.

In order not to exceed the budgetary constraint we know, from the previous numerical example, that the possible values of n_1, n_2 and n_3 are: 1, 2, 1; 2, 1, 1; and 3, 1, 1 respectively. Table 8.1 can now be

Table 8.1

Equipment configuration (n_1, n_2, n_3)	Equipment reliability	Equipment safety
(1, 2, 1)	0·737	0·041
(2, 1, 1)	0·624	0·061
(3, 1, 1)	0·629	0·090

constructed which gives equipment reliability and safety probabilities for these three alternatives. It is seen that both alternatives (1, 2, 1) and (2, 1, 1) meet the safety constraint of 0·075 but (1, 2, 1) is the optimal design since it also maximizes the reliability.

Sample calculation
When $n_1 = 2$, $n_2 = 1$, $n_3 = 1$ then:

Equipment reliability: $(1 - 0.2^2)(1 - 0.3)(1 - 0.1) = 0.624$
Equipment safety: $(1 - 0.95^2)(1 - 0.3)(1 - 0.1) = 0.061$
Equipment cost: $2000 \times 2 + 3000 + 1000 = £8000$

8.4.4 FURTHER COMMENTS
Since the numerical example was relatively simple an enumeration of the consequences of all possible design configurations was possible. If this is not convenient then the reader may refer to Bellman and Dreyfus (cited in Section 8.3.4) for a dynamic programming approach. The interested reader may wish to refer to Roberts [40] who discusses briefly problems of premature operation of series/parallel systems.

In the example it has been assumed that premature operation of the system could occur if one component in the first stage operated because of a spurious input signal. To reduce further the probability of premature operation it might be possible to design the stage so that at least r of the n components would have to operate before a signal would be passed to the next stage. Such a procedure is termed voting redundancy. The appropriate mathematics is given in many textbooks on reliability (see Rau [39] and Shooman [42]).

8.5 Optimal mix of redundancy/design effort to minimize the total cost of achieving at least a specified level of reliability

8.5.1 STATEMENT OF PROBLEM

Equipment, composed of one stage, is required to be designed to operate for one unit of time, say a year, at an availability (equivalent to reliability) at least equal to that specified by the equipment user.

The design team can meet this requirement through the use of standby redundancy within the stage or by designing equipment which can meet the availability requirement without using redundancy. The design of such a reliable equipment is costly and a balance is required between the amount of money spent in design and the use of redundancy, thus using cheaper and less reliable components, to meet the availability requirement.

8.5.2 CONSTRUCTION OF MODEL

(1) p_j is the probability of successful operation for a unit of time of a component of type j, j takes the values $1, 2, \ldots, m$, with component of type 1 being less reliable than type 2, type 2 being less reliable than type 3, etc.

The reliability of equipment composed of one stage, having n components of type j in parallel is, from (*c*) of Section 8.2,

$$R_e = (1 - q_j^{n_j})$$

(2) The design and operation cost of a component of type j for one unit of time is $A + Bj$ where A and B are constants. This is illustrated in Figure 8.8.

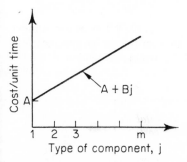

Fig. 8.8

(3) The fixed cost of a component is F, independent of design specification.

(4) The equipment reliability must equal at least R.

The problem is to determine the optimal type of component, j, to design and the optimal number of these to have in parallel in the equipment to minimize the total cost of the equipment over one unit of time, subject to a reliability restriction. Thus we wish to

Minimize $[n_j F + (A + Bj)n_j]$ total cost   (8.3)
$j = 1, 2 \ldots m$
  subject to $(1 - q_j^{n_j}) \geqslant R$ reliability constraint

This is a model of the problem relating type of component j, and number of components of type j in parallel, n_j, to total cost and equipment reliability.

8.5.3 NUMERICAL EXAMPLE

(1) A component of type 1, i.e. $j = 1$, has a probability of
successful operation of 0·75
2, i.e. $j = 2$,   0·80
3, i.e. $j = 3$,   0·85
4, i.e. $j = 4$,   0·90
5, i.e. $j = 5$,   0·95

Thus the q_j values are: $q_1 = 0·25$, $q_2 = 0·20$, $q_3 = 0·15$, $q_4 = 0·10$, $q_5 = 0·05$.

(2) The fixed cost of a component is £1000. The variable cost, which depends on the reliability specification of the component, is £$(500 + 1000j)$.

(3) The equipment reliability must be at least 0·95.
Thus, from the model we wish to:

Minimize $[n_j 1000 + (500 + 1000j)n_j]$
$j = 1, 2 \ldots m$
  subject to $(1 - q_j^{n_j}) \geqslant 0·95$.

For the different types of components, Table 8.2 gives the number of components required, in parallel, to meet the design specification, the actual equipment reliability, and the associated total cost.

Table 8.2

Type of component, j	Number of components in parallel, n_j	R_e	Total cost
1	3	0·98	7500
2	2	0·96	7000
3	2	0·98	9000
4	2	0·99	11000
5	1	0·95	6500

Thus it is seen that the use of components of type 1 or of type 2 give the same minimal total cost value.

Sample calculation
If $j = 2$, then

$$1 - (0 \cdot 20)^{n_2} \geqslant 0 \cdot 95$$

Thus $n_2 = 2$.
This gives $R_e = 1 - (0 \cdot 20)^2 = 0 \cdot 96$.
When $j = 2$, $n_2 = 2$, the total cost is

$$2 \times 1000 + 500 + 1000 \times 2 = £4500$$

8.5.4 FURTHER COMMENTS
An obvious extension of the problem of this section is to equipment composed of several stages, and not just one. An interesting extension covered by Sandler [41] is the use of equipment over several periods of time and the inclusion of increasing operating costs per unit of time into the model. Selection of the optimal design configuration is then based on the total cost of design and operation over the period that the equipment is required. Sandler uses an exponential trend in design costs, rather than a linear trend as used in the above numerical example.

8.6 Optimal degree of component redundancy: minimization of total cost of operation and downtime

8.6.1 STATEMENT OF PROBLEM
It is required to design and operate equipment which is composed of one stage, but which can have several components in parallel within the stage. The purpose of this standby redundancy is to reduce the proportion of time that the equipment is inoperable due to all components being in a failed state since operation of the equipment only requires one component to function. Increasing redundancy results in increased costs of components in the equipment and routine maintenance costs of these components. A balance is required between these component costs and downtime cost which reduces with increased redundancy.

8.6.2 CONSTRUCTION OF MODEL
(1) The probability that a component will operate for one unit of time is p, therefore the probability that it will not operate for the unit of time, $q = 1 - p$.

(2) The probability that the equipment will operate for the unit of time is $1 - q^n$ where n is the number of components in parallel in the stage. $1 - q^n$ is defined as the reliability of the equipment. It is also the long run availability per unit time of the equipment.

(3) The long run unavailability, or downtime per unit time, of the equipment is q^n.

(4) The capital cost per component per unit time is c_c.

(5) The routine operating cost per component for one unit of time is c_o.

(6) The total cost of downtime for one unit of time is c_d.

(7) The objective is to determine the optimal number of components n to minimize the total cost per unit time of capital, operating and downtime costs. Letting $C(n)$ be this total cost then

$C(n)$ = Capital cost per unit time
      + Operating cost per unit time
      + Downtime cost per unit time
    = $nc_c + c_o$ (proportion of time a component is working)
      + c_d (proportion of time equipment is failed)

Therefore

$$C(n) = nc_c + nc_o(1 - q^n) + c_d q^n \qquad (8.4)$$

This is a model of the problem relating component number n to total cost $C(n)$.

8.6.3 NUMERICAL EXAMPLE

Letting $p = 0.95$, i.e. $q = 0.05$, $c_c =$ £250, $c_o =$ £2000, $c_d =$ £100000 then equation (8.4) becomes

$$C(n) = 250n + n2000(1 - 0.05^n) + 100000 \times q^n$$

Table 8.3 gives the values of $C(n)$ for various values of n. Thus it is seen that the optimal number of components to have in parallel in the equipment is 2.

Table 8.3

n	1	2	3	4
$C(n)$	7150	4850	6783	8800

8.6.4 FURTHER COMMENTS

As with the example of the previous section the equipment configuration considered in the sample was relatively simple. Without difficulty the model could be extended to cater for equipment composed of several stages.

8.7 Optimal level of active parallel redundancy for an equipment with components subject to repair

8.7.1 STATEMENT OF PROBLEM

As part of a production system there are n machines in parallel whose output is fed into the next stage of the process. If one of these n machines fails, then the production load is redistributed amongst the remaining $(n - 1)$ operating machines, with no reduction in throughput. The failed machine is then repaired and eventually returned to the system. It will be assumed that one machine would, if necessary, cope with the workload and so production losses would only be incurred if all n machines were in a failed state. The problem is to determine the optimal number of machines to have in parallel to minimize the total cost per unit time of operation and downtime losses of the stage.

8.7.2 CONSTRUCTION OF MODEL

(1) The failure distribution of a machine is negative exponential with mean time to failure $1/\lambda$.

(2) The time required to repair a failed machine is negative exponentially distributed with mean service time $1/\mu$.

(3) Given that there are n machines in parallel in a stage and the stage then becomes failed due to the nth machine failing (all others having previously failed and not yet repaired), the mean proportion of unit time that the stage is in a failed state, thus incurring downtime, is $d(n)$ where*

$$d(n) = \frac{\rho^n}{(1 + \rho)^n} \qquad \text{with } \rho = \lambda/\mu$$

---

* Derivation of the formula was based on queueing theory, noting that the proportion of unit time the stage is down is equivalent to the probability that, at any time, all n machines are in a failed state. It assumes that a repair crew is available for each machine so that whenever a machine fails, repair can start immediately. A useful reference from which downtime formulae can be obtained when there are restrictions on the number of available repair crews is Chapter 6 of Rau [39].

(4) The cost of one unit of downtime is C_d.

(5) The total cost of operation per unit time for one machine is C_o.

(6) The objective is to determine the optimal number of machines n to have in parallel in the stage to minimize the total cost per unit time of operation and downtime losses. Letting $C(n)$ be this total cost,

$$C(n) = \text{Number of machines in parallel}$$
$$\times \text{ Cost per machine per unit time}$$
$$+ \text{ Proportion of unit time that stage is failed}$$
$$\times \text{ Cost of downtime per unit time}$$

Therefore

$$C(n) = nC_o + d(n)C_d \qquad (8.5)$$

This is a model of the problem relating the number of machines in parallel n to total cost $C(n)$.

8.7.3 NUMERICAL EXAMPLE

Letting $\lambda = 20$ failures per unit time, $1/\mu = 0.05$, $C_o = £100$, $C_d = £500$ then equation (8.5) becomes

$$C(n) = n100 + d(n)500$$

Evaluation of the above equation for various values of n enables Table 8.4 to be constructed. Thus it is seen that the optimal number of machines in parallel in the stage is 2.

Table 8.4

n	$d(n)$	$C(n)$
1	0·500 00	350·000
2	0·250 00	325·000
3	0·125 00	375·500
4	0·062 50	436·250
5	0·031 25	518·125

8.7.4 FURTHER COMMENTS

In the above problem it has been assumed that the failure distribution of a machine remained constant and was not influenced by, for example, an increase in its production load due to another machine in the stage failing. If, however, it was felt necessary to incorporate an increasing probability of machine failure due to an increase in its load then it would be necessary to derive a new expression for $d(n)$, the mean proportion of unit time that the stage is down.

Also it was assumed that the system would only be completely failed once all machines in parallel were in a failed state. In such parallel redundancy problems, where all machines operate, failure of the system may occur when r of the n parallel machines are in a failed state. If such is the case, then a new expression for $d(n)$ would need to be determined.

9 Scheduling and Sequencing Decisions

9.1 Introduction

The words "scheduling" and "sequencing" are frequently used interchangeably to describe a given problem situation. However in this chapter we will use the following distinct definitions.

Scheduling problems are concerned with determining the timing of arrivals or departures of units requiring, or giving, a service. (Thus, for example, a bus timetable is a schedule of the planned arrivals and departures of buses; a project plan is a schedule of the times when constituent jobs of the project can, or must, start and finish.)

Sequencing problems are concerned with determining the order in which units requiring a service are served. (Thus, for example, a failed equipment which arrives at a maintenance workshop may have to wait in a queue before it can be repaired. Perhaps depending on priorities attached to the various failed equipments in the queue the sequence in which these equipments will be repaired will be determined.)

9.2 Scheduling decisions

Since application of the principles of project network analysis to aid scheduling decisions in maintenance will be well known to readers concerned with project scheduling, such as scheduling maintenance work required to be completed during the annual shutdown of a plant, this area of maintenance decision-making will not be discussed in any detail in this book.

Project network techniques is becoming the generic name given to scheduling procedures which have in the past been labelled as, for example, PERT (program evaluation and review technique), CPM (critical path method), and CPS (critical path scheduling), and those described as activity-on-node systems including the method of potentials and precedence diagrams, since the basis of all these procedures is the construction of a graphical representation (termed a network) of a project composed of a number of constituent jobs.

There are now many computer packages available to perform the calculations necessary for project scheduling. As well as covering the calculations necessary for only a "time analysis" of the project these packages can often take account of cost analysis and resource restrictions. Readers wishing to have an introduction to the use of network techniques for project scheduling, which presupposed the sequencing specification of constituent jobs of the project, may refer to any one of a number of books on the subject (see, for example, Battersby [3] and Moder and Phillips [32]).

9.3 Sequencing decisions

In the introduction to this chapter we said that an example of sequencing was the way in which jobs requiring the facilities of machines in a workshop were serviced. To illustrate the complexity of this problem area consider a very simple example in which we have three jobs, 1, 2 and 3, waiting to be serviced on one machine, machine *A*. This is illustrated in Figure 9.1. In this example there are 3! possible

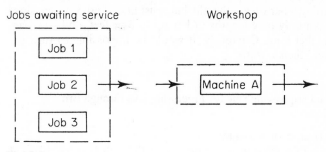

Fig. 9.1

sequences of getting the three jobs completed. The six possible sequences are given in Table 9.1.

Table 9.1

First job on machine A	Second job on machine A	Third job on machine A
1	2	3
1	3	2
2	1	3
2	3	1
3	1	2
3	2	1

If, however, instead of there being only one machine through which each job has to pass, each job has to pass in any sequence through 2 machines, A and B, also in any order, there would be $(3!)^2 \times 2 = 72$ possible sequences. In general, if there are n jobs requiring servicing on m machines, in any order, then there are $(n!)^m \times m!$ possible sequences of getting the n jobs completed. Thus it can be seen that even for relatively simple sequencing problems there are a very large number of sequences possible and what we wish to determine is the optimal sequence.

The sequence to be adopted will, of course, depend on what is meant by optimal. Possible optimal sequences may be those which minimize total elapsed time (i.e., time from the start of a set of jobs to their finish) or minimize total tardiness (where tardiness of a job is defined as: "completion time"–"due date", when completion time is later than due date, otherwise tardiness is zero).

Before proceeding with some sequencing problems, it is important to note that not all of the $(n!)^m \times m!$ sequences of n jobs on m machines may be possible, due to technological constraints, i.e. some operations on a job may have to be performed in a specific order. For example, before turning a bar on a lathe, the bar must first of all be sawn, since the lathe can only take lengths of bar up to four feet, and new bars are twenty feet long. Obviously, it would be impossible to turn the bar first, and then saw it.

9.4 Optimal sequencing rule for processing jobs through two machines

9.4.1 STATEMENT OF PROBLEM
There are n jobs waiting to be processed through two machines A and B, and no passing is allowed. No passing means that whichever job is processed first on machine A must be processed first on machine B; whichever job is the nth processed on machine A, must be the nth processed on machine B. In practice, the no-passing constraint may arise when jobs are moving down a production line, conveyed on overhead cranes or conveyors, or in pipes. It will also be assumed that jobs passing from one machine to another can be held in storage between machines, if a machine is not free to accept the job. The problem is to determine a sequencing rule which will minimize the total elapsed time for processing the n jobs.

9.4.2 CONSTRUCTION OF MODEL
(1) We will assume that all jobs are first worked on machine A and then machine B.

(2) Let

A_i = time required by job i on machine A

B_i = time required by job i on machine B

T = total elapsed time for completion of jobs $1, 2, \ldots, n$

I_i = idle time on machine B from end of job $i - 1$ to start of job i

where $i = 1, 2, \ldots, n$.

These parameters are illustrated on the bar chart of Figure 9.2 when there are three jobs to be processed on machines A and

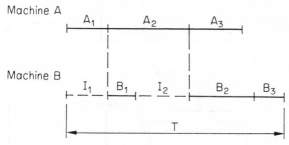

Fig. 9.2

B and the sequence is job 1, then job 2, then job 3.

(3) The flow chart of Figure 9.3 is based on an algorithm developed by Johnson [24] (see also Muth and Thomson [34]) which results in identification of an optimal sequence to minimize the total elapsed time of processing n jobs through two machines, with no passing allowed, and with the jobs going to machine A first, then machine B. If the jobs went to machine B first, then machine A, the same solution procedure is applicable, remembering that machine B would be equivalent to machine A in the flow chart of Figure 9.3 and machine A equivalent to machine B.

9.4.3 NUMERICAL EXAMPLE

There are four jobs to be processed, first on machine A, then on machine B. No passing is allowed. The problem is to determine a sequence for processing these jobs to minimize the total elapsed time for getting the four jobs completed. The processing times required for these jobs on machines A and B are given in Table 9.2.

Table 9.2

Job no. i	Processing time required on machine A for job i A_i	Processing time required on machine B for job i B_i
1	3	1
2	8	1
3	5	8
4	2	9

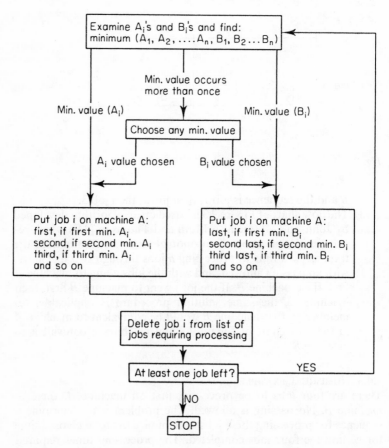

Fig. 9.3

Application of the flow chart of the sequencing algorithm (Figure 9.3) proceeds as follows:

Step 1: Min $(3, 8, 5, 2; 1, 1, 8, 9) = 1$ and occurs for job 1 or job 2 on machine B (i.e. B_1 or B_2).

Step 2: Select job 1 on machine B (i.e. B_1 is chosen).

Step 3: Put job 1 on machine A last.

Step 4: Delete job 1 from set of jobs, (i.e. $-, 8, 5, 2; -, 1, 8, 9$)

Step 5: Min $(-, 8, 5, 2; -, 1, 8, 9) = 1$ and occurs for job 2 on machine B (i.e. B_2).

Step 6: (Second time a B value is a minimum.) Put job 2 on machine A, second last.

Step 7: Delete job 2 from set of jobs, (i.e. $-, -, 5, 2; -, -, 8, 9$)

Step 8: Min $(-, -, 5, 2; -, -, 8, 9) = 2$ and occurs for job 4 on machine A (i.e. A_4).

Step 9: (First time an A value is a minimum.) Put job 4 on machine A first.

Step 10: Delete job 4 from set of jobs, (i.e. $-, -, 5, -; -, -, 8, -$).

Step 11: Min $(-, -, 5, -; -, -, 8, -) = 5$ and occurs for job 3 on machine A (i.e. A_3).

Step 12: (Second time an A value is a minimum.) Put job 3 on machine A second.

Note that for the last job it will always be obvious where it should be placed in the job sequence. If the processing times were such that the sequence was based on B values only for $(n - 1)$ jobs, then the nth job to be sequenced would go on machine A first. If the sequence was based on A values only for $(n - 1)$ jobs the nth job to be sequenced would go last on machine A. If the sequence is based on a mixture of A_i and B_i values then there will only be one possible place to sequence the last job on machine A.

The sequencing of this example is illustrated in Figure 9.4 from which it is seen that the minimum total elapsed time to process the 4 jobs on the two machines is 21 units.

9.4.4 FURTHER COMMENTS

If there are two or three machines then for the problem of Section 9.4 there will never be any advantage in changing the sequence of jobs from one machine to another. However, if there are more than three machines then it may be of advantage to change the ordering. These points are proved by Johnson [24].

The problem posed in 9.4 is basically very simple. Algorithms for dealing with other sequencing problems have been developed but again they can cater only for "simple" problems, for example, n jobs to be

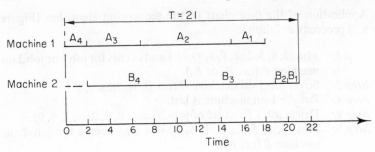

Fig. 9.4

processed through three machines; two jobs to be processed through *m* machines.

The reader should be aware that a different method for solving a three machine sequencing problem is given by Lomnicki [29].

9.5 Optimal sequence of getting machines overhauled by three maintenance crews

9.5.1 STATEMENT OF PROBLEM

During the annual shut-down of a plant there are *n* machines requiring the attention of three maintenance crews, say a crew of fitters (*A*) who disassemble the *n* machines; a crew of electricians (*B*) who replace particular parts of the machines; and finally, a further crew of fitters (*C*) who re-assemble and test the machines. It will be assumed that no passing is allowed, i.e. once the first crew starts to dismantle a machine the following two crews must then do their work on that machine before proceeding to another machine. The problem is to determine the sequence in which *n* machines are attended to, to minimize the total time of getting the *n* machines overhauled.

9.5.2 CONSTRUCTION OF MODEL

(1) There are *n* machines requiring the attention of crews *A*, *B* and *C*.

(2) A_i, B_i and C_i are the times required to be spent by maintenance crews *A*, *B* and *C* on the *i*th machine, $i = 1, 2 \ldots, n$.

(3) Provided at least one of the following conditions is met:

     (i) min. $A_i \geqslant$ max. B_i
     (ii) min. $C_i \geqslant B_i$

then the flow chart of Figure 9.3, which can be used to determine the optimal sequence of getting *n* machines attended to by two maintenance crews to minimize the total time of getting the n machines completed, can also be used when there are three maintenance crews. The sums D_i and E_i are formed, where $D_i = A_i + B_i$ and $E_i = B_i + C_i$, and in the flow chart D_i and E_i then replace A_i and B_i respectively.

9.5.3 NUMERICAL EXAMPLE

There are six machines which require attention by three maintenance crews. The times required by each crew are given in Table 9.3 and

Table 9.3

Machine i	Time required by crew A, A_i	Time required by crew B, B_i	Time required by crew C, C_i
1	8	3	6
2	6	2	5
3	12	4	8
4	4	1	4
5	6	2	5
6	8	3	6

Table 9.4

Machine i	$A_i + B_i = D_i$	$B_i + C_i = E_i$
1	11	9
2	8	7
3	16	12
4	5	5
5	8	7
6	11	9

given these values Table 9.4 can be formed. Application of the flow chart of the sequencing algorithm (Figure 9.3) results in the sequence given in Table 9.5.

The calculations required to determine the sequence given in Table 9.5 are as follows

Step 1: Check that conditions specified in (3) of Section 9.5.2 are met.

Table 9.5

Sequence	Machine no.
1st machine to be attended to	4
2nd machine to be attended to	3
3rd machine to be attended to	6
4th machine to be attended to	1
5th machine to be attended to	5
6th machine to be attended to	2

Step 2: min $(11, 8, 16, 5, 8, 11; 9, 7, 12, 5, 7, 9)$
= 5 which occurs as D_4 or E_4 value. Select D_4.
Therefore machine 4 is attended first by crew A.

Step 3: min $(11, 8, 16, -, 8, 11; 9, 7, 12, -, 7, 9)$
= 7 which occurs as E_2 or E_5. Select E_2.
Therefore machine 2 is attended last by crew A.

Step 4: min $(11, -, 16, -, 8, 11; 9, -, 12, -, 7, 9)$
= 7 which occurs as E_5.
Therefore machine 5 is attended to second last by crew A.

Step 5: min $(11, -, 16, -, -, 11; 9, -, 12, -, -, 9)$
= 9 which occurs for E_1 or E_6. Select E_1.
Therefore machine 1 is attended third last by crew A.

Step 6: min $(-, -, 16, -, -, 11; -, -, 12, -, -, 9)$
= 9 which occurs for E_6.
Therefore machine 6 is attended to fourth last by crew A.

Step 7: There is only machine 3 left, therefore it must be the second machine to be attended to by crew A.

Figure 9.5 illustrates the time consequences of the optimal sequence from which it is seen that the required maintenance of the six machines will have a total duration of 51 units. The dotted lines indicate idle time of the maintenance crews.

9.5.4 FURTHER COMMENTS

The dotted lines in Figure 9.5 following the completion of crews B and C's work on machine 4 can be thought of as unnecessary idle time of machines incurred due to machines having to wait until the

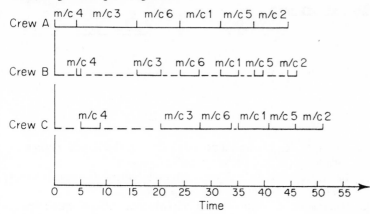

Fig. 9.5

maintenance crew has finished earlier machines. For a continuous production process the problem of minimizing the total time of maintaining the six machines has been viewed as one of minimizing the unnecessary idle time of the machines by Miller and Starr [31] Their problem refers to downtime in a refinery where contract labour is used, at a cost, to assist in the maintenance work. The specific objective of the Miller and Starr analysis was to minimize the idle time of the maintenance crews subject to returning each refinery to operation as soon as possible.

It is probably fair to say that the state of research and application of optimal sequencing rules is limited. Wild [50] gives a good introduction to the possible methods which can be used to assist in sequencing problems, such as mathematical programming, branch-and-bound and priority rule despatching.

References

[1] BARLOW, R. E., and PROCHAN, F., *Mathematical Theory of Reliability* (Wiley, 1965) pp. 114–17.

[2] BARTHOLOMEW, D. J., Two-stage replacement strategies, *Operational Research Quarterly*, vol. 14 (1963).

[3] BATTERSBY, A., *Network Analysis* (Macmillan/St. Martin's Press, 1967).

[4] BELLMAN, R., Equipment replacement policy, *Journal of the Society for Industrial and Applied Mathematics (SIAM)*, vol. 3 (1955) pp. 133–6.

[5] BELLMAN, R. E., and DREYFUS, S., *Applied Dynamic Programming* (Oxford University Press/Princeton University Press, 1962).

[6] BENSON, F., and COX, D. R., The productivity of machines requiring attention at random intervals, *Journal of the Royal Statistical Society*, Series B, vol. 13 (1951).

[7] BRENDER, D. M., *A surveillance model for recurrent events*, I.B.M. Corporation, Watson Research Center, Yorktown Heights, New York, Research Report RC-837 (1962).

[8] BUCKLAND, W. R., *Statistical Assessment of the Life Characteristic* (Griffin, 1964).

[9] CARRUTHERS, A. J., MACGOW, I., and HACKEMER, G. C., A study of the optimum size of plant maintenance gangs, *Operational Research in Maintenance*, ed. A. K. S. Jardine (Manchester University Press/Barnes and Noble, 1970).

[10] TOCHER, K. D., *The Art of Simulation* (E.U.P. 1967).

[11] COCHRANE, W. G., *Sampling Techniques* (Wiley, 1963).

[12] COX, D. R., *Renewal Theory* (Methuen/Wiley, 1962).

[13] COX, D. R., and SMITH, W. L., *Queues* (Chapman and Hall, 1961).

[14] CROWTHER, J. G., and WHIDDINGTON, R., *Science at War* (H.M.S.O., 1963).

[15] DAVIDSON, D., An overhaul policy for deteriorating equipment, *Operational Research in Maintenance*, ed. A. K. S. Jardine (Manchester University Press/Barnes and Noble, 1970).

[16] DE GARMO, E. P., and CANADA, J. R., *Engineering Economy* (Collier-Macmillan, 1973).

[17] EILON, S., KING, J. R., and HUTCHINSON, D. E., A study in

equipment replacement, *Operational Research Quarterly*, vol. 17, no. 1 (1966).

[18] GREENSTED, C. S., JARDINE, A. K. S., and MACFARLANE, J. D., *Statistical Methods in Quality Control* (Heinemann, 1974).

[19] HADLEY, G., and WHITIN, T. M., *Analysis of Inventory Systems* (Prentice-Hall, 1963).

[20] HASTINGS, N. A. J., Equipment replacement and the repair limit method, *Operational Research in Maintenance*, ed. A. K. S. Jardine (Manchester University Press/Barnes and Noble, 1970).

[21] HASTINGS, N. A. J., and PEACOCK, J. B., *Statistical Distributions* (Butterworth, 1974).

[22] HOWARD, R. A., *Dynamic Programming and Markov Processes* (Wiley, 1960).

[23] JARDINE, A. K. S. (ed.), *Operational Research in Maintenance* (Manchester University Press/Barnes and Noble, 1970).

[24] JOHNSON, S. M., Optimal two- and three-stage production schedules with set-up times included, *Naval Research Logistics Quarterly*, vol. 1 (1954).

[25] JORGENSON, D. W., MCCALL, J. J., and RADNOR, R., *Optimal Replacement Policy* (North-Holland, 1967).

[26] LEE, A. M., *Applied Queueing Theory* (Macmillan/St. Martin's Press, 1966).

[27] LEWIS, C. D., *Scientific Inventory Control* (Butterworth, 1970).

[28] LINDLEY, D. V., and MILLER, J. C. P., *Cambridge Elementary Statistical Tables* (Cambridge University Press, 1964).

[29] LOMNICKI, Z. A., A branch-and-bound algorithm for the exact solution of three-machine scheduling problem, *Operational Research Quarterly*, vol. 16 (1965) pp. 89–100.

[30] MERRET, A. J., and SYKES, A., *The Finance and Analysis of Capital Projects* (Longmans, 1963).

[31] MILLER, D. W., and STARR, M. K., *Executive Decisions and Operations Research* (Prentice-Hall, 1960).

[32] MODER, J. J., and PHILLIPS, C. R., *Project Management with CPM and PERT* (Van Nostrand Reinhold, 1964).

[33] MORSE, P. M., *Queues, Inventories and Maintenance* (Wiley, 1963).

[34] MUTH, J. F., and THOMSON, G. L. (eds.), *Industrial Scheduling* (Prentice-Hall, 1963).

[35] NAIK, M. D., and NAIR, K. P. K., Multi-stage replacement strategies, *Operations Research*, vol. 13 (1965).

[36] NAYLOR, T. H., BALINTFKY, J. L., BURDICK, D. S., and CHU, K., *Computer Simulation Techniques* (Wiley, 1966).

[37] PECK, C. G., and HAZELWOOD, R. N., *Finite Queueing Tables* (Wiley, 1958).

[38] PIERUSHKA, E., *Principles of Reliability* (Prentice-Hall, 1963).

[39] RAU, J. G., *Optimization and Probability in Systems Engineering* (Van Nostrand Reinhold, 1970).

[40] ROBERTS, N. H., *Mathematical Methods in Reliability Engineering*, (McGraw-Hill, 1964).

[41] SANDLER, G. H., *System Reliability Engineering* (Prentice-Hall, 1963).

[42[SHOOMAN, M. L., *Probabilistic Reliability: An Engineering Approach* (McGraw-Hill, 1968).

[43] SMITH, W. L., Regenerative stochastic processes, *Proceedings of the Royal Statistical Society*, A, vol. 232 (1955).

[44] STUART, A., *Basic Ideas of Scientific Sampling* (Griffin, 1962).

[45] TERBORGH, G., *Dynamic Equipment Policy* (McGraw-Hill, 1949).

[46] THOMAS, A. B., *Stock Control in Manufacturing Industries* (Gower Press, London, 1968).

[47] WAGNER, H. M., *Principles of Operations Research* (Prentice-Hall, 1969).

[48] WHITE, D. J., *Dynamic Programming* (Oliver and Boyd/Holden-Day, 1969).

[49] WHITE, D. J., DONALDSON, W. A., and LAWRIE, N. L., *Operational Research Techniques*, vol. 1 (Business Books, 1969).

[50] WILD, R., *The Techniques of Production Management* (Holt, Reinhart and Winston, 1971).

[51] WILKINSON, R. I., Working curves for delayed exponential calls served in random order, *Bell System Technical Journal*, vol. 32 (1953). Figure 19 in this Journal is copyright of the American Telephone and Telegraph Company 1953 and is reproduced by permission.

[52] WOODMAN, R. C., Replacement policies for components that deteriorate, *Operational Research Quarterly*, vol. 18, no. 2 (1967).

[53] AITCHESON, J., and BROWN, J. A. C., *The Log-Normal Distribution* (Cambridge University Press, 1969).

Index